ROAD MAKING AND
ROAD USING

Frontispiece

A HEAVILY TRAFFICKED STREET (PARK LANE, LONDON)
PAVED WITH ROUGHENED ASPHALT

(Photo: W. H. Brookman, Studio Service, London, E.C.3)

ROAD MAKING
AND
ROAD USING

BY

T. SALKIELD

M.INST.C.E.

Formerly City Engineer, Delhi, India

WITH AN APPRECIATION BY

LORD HAILEY

P.C., G.C.S.I., G.C.I.E., G.C.M.G.

FOURTH EDITION

LONDON
SIR ISAAC PITMAN & SONS, LTD.

First published 1927
Reprinted 1934
Second edition 1936
Revised and enlarged 1938
Third edition 1947
Revised reprint 1948
Fourth edition 1953

SIR ISAAC PITMAN & SONS, Ltd.
PITMAN HOUSE, PARKER STREET, KINGSWAY, LONDON, W.C.2
THE PITMAN PRESS, BATH
PITMAN HOUSE, LITTLE COLLINS STREET, MELBOURNE
27 BECKETTS BUILDINGS, PRESIDENT STREET, JOHANNESBURG

ASSOCIATED COMPANIES
PITMAN PUBLISHING CORPORATION
2 WEST 45TH STREET, NEW YORK

SIR ISAAC PITMAN & SONS (CANADA) Ltd.
(INCORPORATING THE COMMERCIAL TEXT BOOK COMPANY)
PITMAN HOUSE, 381–383 CHURCH STREET, TORONTO

MADE IN GREAT BRITAIN AT THE PITMAN PRESS, BATH
E3—(B.6009)

AN APPRECIATION

By Lord Hailey, P.C., G.C.S.I., G.C.I.E., G.C.M.G.

I am glad of this opportunity of welcoming the fourth edition of Major T. Salkield's book. I take the opportunity of repeating here a note which I wrote on the appearance of the third edition of this work.

"The success which has attended Major Salkield's literary and other activities towards the solution of the problems connected with the roads and highways of the United Kingdom has been a source of pleasure, but of little surprise, to those who were acquainted with his work as Municipal Engineer of Delhi, some thirty years ago. Those who visit the old city of Delhi to-day would find it hard to realize the conditions which prevailed before Delhi was adopted as the capital of India, and received the benefit of the measures undertaken, at very considerable cost, to introduce a higher standard of road and sanitary amenities. Its roads were without foundations, perpetually deep in dust or mud; few of the streets had footpaths; there was a malarious swamp on one side of the city walls, and century-old deposits of rubbish outside the others. Open sewers ran through the main thoroughfares; the water supply was totally insufficient; everywhere there was filth, and everywhere flies. In dealing with these conditions, Major Salkield had to rely on a very inadequate establishment, and often had to face much local opposition; but I can speak with personal experience of the substantial improvements he effected—a tribute not less to his resolution and steadfastness of purpose than to his technical ability. They are characteristics which served him equally well during his service in the war of 1914–18, by which the tenure of his post at Delhi was interrupted.

"His book must already be familiar to civil engineers at

home, but it cannot fail to be of interest also to those who will be responsible for carrying out the programme now in contemplation for a great extension of road communications in India, and for the similar measures which the funds made available by the Colonial Development and Welfare Act will make possible in the Colonies. The expansion of road communications is the pre-condition of development in most of our Colonies; its results alike in the social and economic field have had a significance that can well be described as dramatic. But road-making to-day demands a more advanced technique than it did a generation ago; nothing will now serve but the "all-weather" road, capable of standing up to motor traffic, and so engineered as to admit of a really economic use of that form of traffic."

I can only endorse now what I wrote then. Time has merely added to the importance which attaches to the improvement of road communications, and to the obligation we owe to those who, like Major Salkield, have laboured to add to the technical equipment of the civil engineer.

PREFACE
TO THE FOURTH EDITION

THOUGH primarily intended for the student this book may be appreciated by the non-technical reader who is interested in the development of the highway system of the kingdom. For both classes, the student and the non-technical reader, all the chapters which contain data and information, from the historic angle, have been retained. The chapters dealing with modern methods of road construction have, however, been brought up-to-date or as close up-to-date as is possible in these days of rapid development due to scientific and industrial research.

As is evidenced in various chapters, the historic aspect of this subject may be compared with the modern methods of road construction. In this connexion it may with interest be recalled that John Loudon McAdam was right in his theories about road construction. His ideas are now accepted by those who, by training and experience, are capable of forming a judgment. His surname, because of its importance, was admitted into the dictionary of English words, though the spelling was slightly altered.

Why has so favourable a verdict been given about McAdam? Because amongst the many theories he enunciated were three simple though fundamental truths. These were that resiliency rather than rigidity was essential; that stability of a road structure depends upon the bearing capacity of the subsoil; and that compaction was due to the binding together of the angular pieces of stone, now called macadam.

Stabilization of the subsoil, as a preparatory measure, is becoming almost as exact a science as that of road-building. McAdam's idea that the interlocking of the pieces of stone would, without any mortar, form a stable surface was correct in theory but not in practice. The application of his methods, when the heavy steam road-roller came into use, made it necessary to use a slurry of earthy matter and water to consolidate the road structure. The unpopularity of the pre-roller method of consolidation can be realized from the following note which appeared in a publication in 1859, and which marks a retrogression in the development of McAdam's system. The writer of the note tells us that: "Macadamization as at present administered consists of huge lumps of granite flung in loose heaps upon a road and left there in the vague hope that in course of time the narrow wheels of passing vehicles may break them up and finally render them fine and smooth enough for traffic." After 1859, another fifty years had to elapse before "macadamization" could be perfected by the general use of heavy steam road-rollers.

An article which appeared in 1898, laudatory of McAdam, and in a vein strangely reminiscent of the period through which we are now passing—paucity of funds and bolstering up of the railways—records that: "The roads remain in a state of suspended development."

When the roads had again come into their own, made popular by the bicycle and later by the motor-car, even well-known engineers were of opinion that the death-knell of the macadam road had been sounded, as rigidity in road construction was favoured. How wrong they were is evidenced by the survival of the macadam road and the methods of construction now employed.

McAdam always argued that resiliency was an important factor in the behaviour and length of life of all highways. In the case of the water-bound macadam roads, the measure of their resiliency is due to the capacity of the matrix to retain moisture. The stones forming the surface coat of such roads were held together like a mosaic paving, partly by friction, but to a greater extent by the elastic tension of the wet slurry with which such roads were compacted at the time of rolling. The moment this kind of binding mortar became dry the structures were unable to react to the stresses and strains set up by vehicular traffic, and disintegration resulted.

Here was the twentieth-century parallel of the nineteenth-century problem which brought the opinions of McAdam and Telford into conflict, McAdam for resiliency in the design and construction of roads and Telford for rigidity. As all subsoils and road foundations are more or less resilient, reference to them must always be comparative; when, however, the shock-absorbing capacities of the different types of road construction are considered, first place must be given to the whole macadam road.

Before the era of mechanical vehicles, the method introduced by Telford was successful, but such a system, in which interstitial wear never ceases under high-speed loads, can now be questioned. When the road-engineer was moving in the direction of rigidity in the design of roads he was assisted by the vehicle designer, who, with improved springing, tyring, and vibration-absorbing devices for the vehicles, helped to counteract the destructive effects of road rigidity.

Action and reaction being equal and opposite the less rigid the road the fewer the shocks and less the damage to vehicles, and also, a matter of supreme importance, reduced vibration and noise.

To-day, bitumen and tar as a mortar or matrix have taken the place of the slurry to bind together the macadam, with consequent permanence of construction and high vibration-minimizing properties.

T. SALKIELD.

NEW MILTON
HANTS.
November, 1952

ACKNOWLEDGMENTS

The publications of the undermentioned have been consulted by the author who acknowledges with thanks the excerpts he has made—

The Asphalt Roads Association.
The British Standards Institution.
The Cement and Concrete Association.
The Federation of Coated Macadam Industries.
The Road Emulsion Association.
The Limmer and Trinidad Lake Asphalt Company Ltd.

To the last named he also tenders his thanks for some of the illustrations in this book.

PREFACE
TO THE THIRD EDITION

SINCE the Second Edition of this book was published in 1936, the science of road making and using has advanced; and the war, which began in 1939, will ultimately alter the whole economic system. With these two factors the road engineer will have to contend; but, as he is not a gold-standard expert, bi-metallist, or professional economist, it is with the hard facts of engineering and common-sense economy that he will have to deal.

> Men laugh and riot till the feast is o'er,
> Then comes the reckoning and they laugh no more.

After an orgy of spending, the nation will be faced with an empty till, a plethora of services, but a shortage of essential commodities.

Economy, which will become a pressing claim upon the attention of all men, is not obtained by unwise saving. When frugality is necessary, expenditure judicious, and the prudent management of all means secured, by which materials and labour are correctly employed, then real economy is ensured.

It has been alleged that "Our backwardness in economic science has been an index of the danger threatening the industrial and commercial prosperity of this country." As it is not an economy to have bad roads, it becomes an axiom of economic science that roads must be well made and maintained so as to ensure savings in tractive effort, which, *pari ratione*, results in economy in the cost of maintenance of both roads and vehicles. But the most astute student of economics, when a road engineer, must often be puzzled to decide where maintenance expenses finish and capital charges begin. And he has also a lot of hard thinking to do before he recommends complete reconstruction of any road, a decision which is often the most economical

one to pursue, and particularly so where maintenance
charges are excessive.

When this present century opened, steam road-rollers
had not been employed in many places outside urban areas.
In such places the stones for road repairs, often hand-
picked flints from the fields, were heaped on the roadside
and broken by old men. From such heaps the broken
stones were spread on the road and consolidated by the
steel-tyred wheels of all types of horse-drawn vehicles.
Here was "economy" indeed, an economy, however, that
received its death-blow by the agitation of the great bicycle clubs. Then came the motor vehicles, with their
expensive rubber tyres and new ideas about road construction. But, remember, all this in less than fifty years!

Of all the ideas that will be propounded for economies in
road construction and maintenance, none is more promising
than the stabilization of subsoils, as it will make necessary
only the minimum expenditure upon actual foundations.

Whether special motorways are constructed or not, it is
certain that a scheme of farm-to-market roads will have
to be undertaken on a big scale if this nation is to maintain its agricultural industry on an economic basis. This
opens up a wide field in road construction, and soil stabilization points the way by which economies may be secured
in the evolution of this type of essential road, as well as
for the improvement of all the roads which are being subjected to uses for which they were never designed.

Between the proposed system of special motorways and
the system of farm-to-market roads, just referred to, there
exists the old network of streets, roads, and highways
which must continue to function, and in the maintenance
of which it may be possible to introduce economies. It
has long been an accepted axiom that the value of any
road must be judged by capital depreciation plus annual
cost of upkeep; in other words, its valuation as an economic proposition is calculated by the ratio of effective life
to cost plus maintenance.

With all the data of traffic statistics which have been compiled since the rapid growth in science, weight, speed, and intensity of road traffic, it is not yet possible to estimate exactly how any particular road will behave, due to the fact that the traffic passing over it is mixed and may change in character. The war must, inevitably, result in a complete change in our economic conditions and, consequently, introduce new factors into the problems connected with road transport.

To meet further intensified traffic conditions, trunk roads will be divided into separate tracks; but much of the heavy long-distance loads will be diverted to the railways, using all types of roads as feeders, for which reason we should expect that road congestion will be considerably reduced.

The controversies about road widths have ceased to be academic, as it has been proved that wide roads do not give immunity from accident for drivers of vehicles or pedestrians, but, on the contrary, a false sense of security for all road users, and especially for those pedestrians who do not always realize quickly enough the time and distance factor. A 20-ft.-wide unobstructed trackway can carry a large volume of traffic when it is all moving rapidly in the same direction and under efficient automatic control by means of lights at cross roads, an arrangement that could be enhanced by means of automatic gates. At main crossroads, however, it should be possible to provide bridges or an under-and-over uninterrupted flow of traffic.

Footpaths for the use, but primarily for the protection of walkers, will become general; and a system of paths away from the roads will be developed.

Tracks for bicycles will become popular and, where possible, will follow the same routes as the footpaths when these are located away from the roads.

The question of road camber may be considered anew, if it is decided that wide single-tracked roads will never again be built. Camber, convexity or "barrelling" as it was called, in McAdam's day, has been regarded as an essential though unsatisfactory feature of road construction, as it increases the tendency of vehicles to skid and, in extreme cases under slippery conditions, to overturn. There is much to be said in favour of a straight cross-section from kerb to kerb, as it enables the full width of the carriage-way to be used, and affords better traffic control to be maintained at bends and corners. With the present types of road surfacings, which are impervious without slipperiness, and particularly where the road is on a gradient, only the minimum of cross fall is required.

Whether kerbs should be 2, 4, or 6 inches high will be an easy-of-solution problem in all places where it is possible to provide an entirely new alignment for footpaths away from the roads, and especially so in all other places where a wide strip or margin of grass or shrubs, a sort of no man's land, can be provided.

Experience has proved the types of foundations necessary for the various classes of roads, under varying conditions, consequently rule-of-thumb methods to determine these need not be employed.

The surfacing of roads to be constructed or reconstructed under the new order of things will be determined by the information which was acquired in the interval between the two great wars. It is certain that noise and vibration will have to be reduced. To achieve this, a full measure of resilience in the road structure will be required. This, and the avoidance of impact shocks, can be provided by the use of a material of a sufficient thickness, quality, and homogeneity.

The segregation of road traffic, a sound scheme, will enable main improvements to be introduced and will lead to a great reduction in the number of accidents, and make the roads in built-up areas less noisy. Such an arrangement would also lead to economies in the cost of construction, as roads could then be built and maintained in the several categories, viz. for heavy, medium, and light types of traffic. This is another hopeful approach to road economy, as it would make possible the calculation to arrive at ultimate cost or initial cost divided by years of expectant life.

Another real source of road construction and maintenance economy is to be found in the salvage and re-use of old materials, and particularly old Portland cement concrete foundations. This is admitted to be a difficult problem, but now that economy will have to be considered, the subject must be tackled by the responsible road engineers. In the past, much nonsense has appeared in the newspapers about the removal of old concrete foundations in the heavily-trafficked streets, which has been described as unnecessary and wasteful. It is known how very destructive of Portland cement concrete foundations modern high-speed heavy road traffic can be, but, in many cases, unless the concrete is laminated by shear stresses and, consequently, no longer in a monolithic condition, economy by salvage may have to be practised oftener in the future than in the past by the use of two-coat bituminous materials.

Finally, responsibility for the post-war roads will have to be shared by the engineer and architect, as it is desirable that all the ugly features of the road shall be eliminated. The approach to every town should be announced by an architectural feature, and Brighton, with its impressive pylons, at its boundary on the London road, has shown how this can be done with dignified simplicity.

All the points raised in the Preface and Introduction are dealt with at length in this book for the information of the student, and for those rate- and tax-paying citizens who are interested in the subject of road making and road using, but who are neither active nor potential road-engineers.

CONTENTS

PART IV. THE ROAD USER IN RELATION TO ROAD MAKING

ILLUSTRATIONS

INTRODUCTION

SINCE this book was first published in 1927, a considerable advance has been made in our knowledge of the subjects of Road Making and Road Using. The chemist has played an increasingly important part with the engineer and the two together have been assisted by others whose skill, both in research and in the compilation of those statistics which are based upon road-traffic census returns and other associated data, entitles them to be regarded as experts in their several professions.

When the twentieth century was ushered in, the dust nuisance was a great menace to the health, comfort, and well-being of the inhabitants of urban and rural areas, and it became intensified by the introduction of self-propelled vehicles. In the country districts one of the charms of road travel was discounted by the festooning with dust of the trees and hedges along the highways. This grey impalpable powder, which enshrouded everything and everybody within hailing distance of a highway, was produced by the disintegration of the earthy matter that was then used in the construction of water-bound macadam roads. Only those whose memories can recall such discomforts are able to compare the delights of road travel to-day with the days of thirty-five years ago.

In 1905-6 a Royal Commission took evidence on the question of road injury by motor cars. It was an exhaustive inquiry, and no fewer than 122 witnesses—road surveyors, members of Highway Committees, experts from the various technical institutions, motorists and others—were called. Dust was the topic which aroused more complaints than the actual state of the road surfaces, and everybody, even the unpopular motorist of those days, regretted that the nuisance had considerably increased since the introduction of fast-moving vehicles.

We know much more about the causes of dust to-day than they did in 1905–6, but even at that time it was realized that pneumatic tyres and the propelling action of the driving wheels caused the disintegration of water-bound macadam roads. Speed of motor cars was also known to be a contributory factor, and it was held that if a maximum of ten miles an hour could be fixed, the dust nuisance would be mitigated.

The horse did not escape indictment, and it was argued that the percussive strain of his armoured feet on a road was partly responsible for the trouble. But whatever the immediate causes of the nuisance may have been, it was known that the method of water-bound road construction was at fault as dust was formed on all such roads by the drying of the earth particles. The grinding of the stones, an action known as interstitial wear, was also responsible for much dust and considerable damage to the road. The hammer-like action of the horses' feet, and wheels of vehicles, caused the subsoil to creep up through the broken stones to the surface of the road, an action that was accelerated by wet weather when the dust became metamorphosed into mud.

The members of the Royal Commission, with prophetic instinct, took a longer view of the situation than some of the witnesses: they realized that to abolish the dust nuisance it would be necessary to adopt methods other than the water-bound system of road construction.

The rapid increase in the number of motor vehicles, and the dust nuisance, were problems which at that time concerned every European nation. So serious, indeed, was the matter that in the year 1908 a Conference was held which resulted in the establishment of a permanent International Association of Road Congresses.

In 1909 a Road Conference was held in London, and in 1910 Parliament established the Road Board which carried out much research and experimental work. Ultimately the Engineering Standards Committee was formed, road materials were standardized, and more scientific methods of road construction were introduced.

But 1913 is the epoch-making date. In that year the International Road Congress in London witnessed to many improvements in the art and craft of road making, "rule of thumb" methods were ended, and the old water-bound system of road construction was condemned as unsatisfactory and expensive. During that same year the increase in number, speed, weight, and load weights of commercial vehicles added further problems for solution, but much had still to be learned about the forces which operate in the destruction of roads.

The push of the propelling wheels of motor vehicles produces on road surfaces quite different results from those which are caused by the tractive efforts of horse-drawn vehicles. The roads, partly because of their uneven surfaces due to waviness and potholes, were rapidly destroyed by the impact of the new types of motor vehicle as the resistance due to a velocity of only $12\frac{1}{2}$ miles per hour may be three times as great on an uneven surfaced road as on a smooth one. The impact blows of heavy motors were destructive not only of roads and vehicles, but caused also a serious dissipation of energy by increasing the tractive effort in converting the forward propelling power into a lifting force. Old solid rubber tyres were almost as hard as steel, and they could deliver impact blows after striking a one-inch obstruction at 16 miles per hour with a force equal to seven times the static wheel load. An additional factor in this question of impact, due to weight and speed, also existed in the static pressure to which the springs of such vehicles under a heavy load were subjected. On a much worn road the wheels jumped and were forced downwards by the combined forces of gravity and the pressure of the springs. With pneumatic tyres there is now little increase of impact with higher speeds owing to their shock-absorbing capacity.

It was at this juncture that the value of tar as a means of minimizing the dust nuisance became manifest; and soon it was extensively used as the binding matrix, instead of earthy matter, in the construction of macadam roads. Bitumen and asphalt, already better known in America than in this country, began to receive the attention of those interested in the making of dust-proof roads.

In 1928 the British Engineering Standards Committee, owing to the misunderstandings due to faulty nomenclature in the definitions of bitumen and asphalt, appointed a Sectional Committee to deal with the subject. In the year 1913 the International Road Congress in London had already experienced similar difficulties which were met by calling the Section dealing with this part of the subject "Construction of Macadamized Roads bound with Tarry, Bituminous, or Asphaltic Materials."

In 1916 the British Engineering Standards Committee drew attention in their Report to the necessity of maintaining "a sharp line of demarcation" between the several materials so as to prevent confusion. In the preface to the Second Edition of their Report (1918) it is stated: "The drawing up of definitions for the so-called bituminous materials used in road-making, on which much confusion now exists, has been felt to be an essential preliminary to the preparation of Standard Specifications." From this date the engineers and chemists were diligently employed in meeting the ever-increasing demands of motor traffic for a smooth, resilient, dustless road pavement. In 1928 the knowledge that had been gained during the preceding ten years led to the formulation of the first series of standardized specifications for the construction of the various types of asphalt roads.

The short memories of those who had benefited by the skill of the engineers and chemists in the use of bituminous materials (both tar and bitumen) led to complaints, as the new road surfaces, under the action of rapidly revolving rubber wheels of high-speed motor vehicles, became in places polished and slippery. The pendulum had swung completely round from the disintegrated dusty roads to the homogeneous surfaces without even sufficient dust to prevent the skidding accidents which occurred too often to motor vehicles in the charge of careless or inexperienced drivers.

In 1935 the British Standards Institution published a revised set of specifications for Asphalt Road Surfaces which has necessitated the complete rewriting of the chapters dealing with this part of the subject.

The new specifications control not only the proportion of the materials used in road manufacture but also their selection, so that the ultimate surface may provide the greatest degree of safety under all conditions of climate. Two major advantages will, it is believed, result from their adoption. First, the alternating character of road surfaces, due to different types of asphalt construction, will cease, as all such roads will conform in continuous lengths to one pattern. Second, a non-skid road surface. The specifications provide for surfacing with stone chippings, uniformly and evenly distributed at the rate of one ton per 60 square yards, punned and subsequently rolled, so as to become partly embodied in the asphalt surface.

Further important features of the new standard specifications are their provision for the use of natural asphalts, in addition to those previously employed, and for the use of the finer aggregates derived from crushing processes, which are also standardized. This latter feature is of importance in connexion with the development of the stone-quarry industry of Great Britain. The revised specifications embody the experience of six years' progress in road construction and maintenance since the original series of specifications was issued. They may not be the last, as the technique of asphalt road construction is continually expanding to meet the exigencies of traffic.

The scientific and economic use of those materials which form the resilient, waterproof, and noise-reducing roads—tar, bitumen, and their aggregates—affords an endless study in the perfecting of those types of road surfaces known as bituminous.

Development has also been continuous in the evolution of the concrete road, and here, as in other sections of this subject, the application of scientific principles is yielding satisfactory results.

Much is written and more is talked about slippery surfaces which are often incorrectly blamed for some of the many road accidents. In 1935 the Institution of Municipal and County Engineers published the investigations of a Sub-Committee appointed to consider the question of road safety. The Report of the Committee is a valuable contribution to this subject, and the following is an excerpt—

" *Road Conditions.* While it is not the special object of the Council to defend the road, nor to blame other factors, it is natural that they should inquire first as to the extent to which road conditions have been responsible for the lamentable death-roll.

"In 121 cases (less than 2 per cent of the whole) road conditions were the sole or main cause of fatal accidents; in 435 cases (about 6 per cent of the whole) they were a contributory cause.

"It must not be supposed, however, that this total includes only defective or slippery roads. Every cause related to the roads is included. In 218 of these cases, for instance, blind corners are blamed in greater or less degree, and when an accident occurs at a blind corner the Council consider want of care also must be inferred.

"Slippery surfaces were the sole or main cause of only 23 accidents (0·3 per cent) and a contributory cause in 126 cases (1·8 per cent).

"The absence of Street Lighting (or insufficient lighting) was the sole or main cause in 20 cases, and a contributory cause in 110 cases.

"This leaves 59 other cases (less than 1 per cent) where some road condition was the sole or contributory cause."

The increase in the weight of road traffic continues to cause anxiety to those who are responsible for the highways and for those owners whose properties are contiguous to them. Noise and vibration caused by road traffic has become so pressing a problem that the scientists are devoting an ever-increasing attention to the subject, and investigations are proceeding on a large scale. In this matter the vehicles and tyre manufacturers and the road makers are involved, as each must assist the other in the perfecting of methods to achieve the object of the Anti-Noise League, whose motto is "No Needless Noise."

For the elimination of everything that tends to make vehicles noisy, which means the evolution of a road (foundation and surface) that reduces impact noise and vibration to a minimum, we may look with a lively expectation of fulfilment before air transport is perfected—and both are now possible within the span of a single life time.

The roads of this kingdom are costing about a million pounds a week, but when the fact is appreciated that our economic life and well-being are largely dependent upon them, and that the cost amounts to three farthings per head of the population per day, it is realized that the sum is by no means excessive for the maintenance of road transport for both goods and passengers.

PART I: HISTORICAL

CHAPTER I

THE ROAD

" JOHN CITIZEN," a shareholder in this huge National Road Concern, valued at £2,000,000,000, is, together with the transport worker, the engineer, the historian, and the archaeologist, interested, not only in the study of road evolution, but in every other phase of the subject which deals with the highways of the United Kingdom. Imagination enables us to visualize how " in the beginning " the wild animals, in herds of varying numbers, would follow the established routes on land (as the migratory birds do in the air) as the seasons changed, in their pursuit of food, that great incentive to action which predicates the preservation of life.

At some period, again "in the beginning," man entered upon the scene. He also had to live, and to live it was necessary for him to pursue, and to pursue meant that he had to follow the wild animals along their tracks. Because his intelligence was so much greater than theirs, he cleared the tracks, blazed trails, and in this way facilitated his movements.

Times and periods elapsed, and man, when he had become less nomadic in his habits, settled in communities or clans, on sites which had the natural advantages of shelter, water, and fertility of soil. These locations became the nuclei of the villages which emerged from these primitive groups of squatters. But long before each village community had become established the ancient tracks had been converted into routes to connect up the settlements.

Those who may be interested in the subject of the lay-out of these ancient trackways are referred to the book

The Old Straight Track, by J. Watkins. It is a fascinating subject and opens up an interesting field for exploration.

WAR AND ROAD DEVELOPMENT

We know that man has ever been an aggressive creature, discontented, assertive, and selfish, but it is these very attributes, though in our highly developed state of civilization we regard them as venial, which have been the propelling forces throughout the ages, and which still exercise in human affairs a considerable influence for good, as well as for evil. When feuds or inter-clan troubles arose, it would be necessary either to close the routes, or to improve them in such a way that quick movement could be effected.

Recorded history teaches us that, for warlike operations, lines of communication must be kept open; consequently we can assume that our early progenitors knew this truth and acted upon it. Thus can we realize that although tracks and routes came into existence when man preyed upon the animal creation, warlike operations, when man hunted his fellow creature, made improved means of communication necessary.

When the Roman legions converted the ancient British tracks into military roads, these roads, because of the facilities they afforded for rapid movement between camps, were of more importance than the mere number of legions ; for what use could be made of men if the means of transportation were non-existent ?

We have only to recall General Wade's operations in Scotland, during the Scottish Rebellion, to realize how his military movements were facilitated by the wonderful road-making activities associated with his name.

The Great Wars of our days have necessitated such means of communication as had never before been imagined, and roads and railways have been built in a way, and to an extent, which even those in whose hands our destiny was placed only realized as the importance of the subject became evident with the march of events. Thus, it is to be noted that road construction owes more to war's demands than to the methods of evolutionary progress, which operate at slower rates in the intervals between wars, styled periods of peace.

INTRODUCTION OF CARRIAGES

Prior to the introduction of vehicles, pack animals followed along the ancient roads and tracks. These afforded sufficient means of intercommunication for the people who pursued the even tenor of their ways throughout the early Middle Ages.

It was not until the end of the fifteenth century that carriages were introduced into this country, and their introduction made it necessary for the ancient roads and tracks to be improved. These roads had, since the Roman evacuation of the country, been allowed to become derelict, and, in consequence, it would only be in periods of dry weather that they would be passable for wheeled vehicles.

THE TURNPIKE SYSTEM

The year 1663 marks a definite step forward, for then an Act was passed which enabled tolls to be levied for the use of certain roads, and the word " turnpike " became a technical and legal term. In the year 1767 the turnpike system was extended to the whole country. In the year 1754 the following notice appeared in Manchester : " A flying coach, however incredible it may appear, will actually, barring accident, arrive in London in four days and a half after leaving Manchester." At that time the roads were not so much roads as tracks over which travellers passed, chiefly on horseback, and commodities were carried on pack animals. The real position of any people in the scale of civilization may best be ascertained by the state of their roads and means of transportation, and it is the realization of this fact that enables us to appreciate the practical as well as the academic meaning of the term " cost per ton mile "

At the close of the eighteenth century several men were taking an active interest in this subject of road making, but two of them have pre-eminence over all the others—McAdam and Telford. Records of that period make it clear to us that the condition of the roads in this country was then deplorable. From the year 1811 onwards much evidence was taken by Committees appointed by the Houses of Parliament with reference to the subject of roads and vehicles. From the historical point of view these records make most interesting reading, but they have no technical value now. To-day, we are faced with conditions much more complex than those which exercised the minds of the earliest of our moderns, who discovered the lost art of road making.

ENGLISH ROADS AFTER WATERLOO

After the peace which followed Waterloo, the next six years was a period of commercial and social depression, which is clearly indicated by the serious drop in the receipts from road tolls. After 1821, however, the income of the various Turnpike Trusts increased very rapidly, which marked the revival of trade and industry in this country. At that time the mileage of roads which were administered by the various trusts was 24,600, and the annual income from tolls £1,282,715. Between the years 1804 and 1819, toll charges were doubled, but the state of the roads went from bad to worse. Evidence of the numerous witnesses who were examined by the various Committees of the House attributed this most unsatisfactory state of affairs to maladministration of funds, and the total lack of knowledge respecting even the most elementary principles of road construction and maintenance.

THE OLD COACHING DAYS

Many stories are written about the old coaching days and the charms and harms associated with the various transport enterprises. Towards the end of the turnpike period, the average speed of the mail coaches was 8½ miles per hour. In addition to the mails, three outside passengers were carried, but the stage coaches carried twelve passengers. The weight of a post or mail coach, when fully loaded, was about 2 tons, and the heavier types of coach 2½ tons. Controversy was continuous with regard to the destruction of the roads, owing to the weight carried, and much difference of opinion existed as to the size and type of wheels, and the width of tyres. Broad wheeled wagons were at one time exempted from toll, on the pretext that they rolled in the loose stones on the roads. The tolls were very excessive, and averaged 3½d. per mile for a coach with four horses, and the number of toll bars caused so much delay and annoyance that they were termed by travellers of that period, "a very galling species of despotism."

ROAD DEVELOPMENT UNDER GEORGE IV

Such a condition of things could not, of course, be allowed to continue in so progressive a period as that which marked the accession of George IV on the death of his father in 1820. The mind of both rulers and ruled was then bent on reform—parliamentary reform, commercial reform, social reform, religious reform. Together with these, improvement and reform of another kind were being introduced. Trade and manufactures had grown, canals, made early in the previous reign, were unable to meet the requirements of commerce, and, consequently, vehicular traffic became more and more necessary. In the year 1827 the Metropolitan turnpikes were abolished by Act of Parliament, and as other similar Acts followed in fairly quick succession, turnpikes from time to time were made free by the compensation of those who had vested interests in them. Freedom for transport followed, trade expanded, intercommunication was made easier, money exchanged hands more rapidly, and the pleasure of travel was made possible for an ever-widening circle of the people.

Wade, Telford, and McAdam are the three men who stand pre-eminent in the history of our highways, as they brought order out of chaos by the introduction of scientific methods in road making.

GENERAL GEORGE WADE

George Wade (1673-1748) was a British Field Marshal who distinguished himself both in war and peace-time pursuits. The Rebellion of 1745 gave an impetus to road making in Scotland with which his name is associated in this couplet—

"Had you seen these roads before they were made
You'd lift up your hands and bless General Wade."

His old Regiment, the 10th (now the Lincolns), did the manual work on the military roads. Wade called them "my highwaymen," and was proud of the work they did and showed his approval when each road was completed by roasting oxen whole. The poet Southey, in his *Journal of a Tour in Scotland* which he made with Telford, described a portrait of General Wade. "He is depicted with a blue velvet robe over his breast-plate and a wig; the countenance mild and pleasing, by no means deficient in intellect, but not indicating a strong mind." Southey, who criticizes the General's bridges, was perhaps prejudiced as he had so high an opinion of his great engineer friend Telford. General Wade built the road between Newcastle and Carlisle, in the making of which he removed long sections of the ancient Roman Wall.

THOMAS TELFORD

This eminent engineer, the son of a poor shepherd of Westerkirk in Eskdale, was born in the year 1757, died in 1834, and was buried in Westminster Abbey. He was known when a boy as "Laughing Tom," and herded the sheep and cows of the farmers in the place of his birth. At the age of 15 he took up the trade of a mason, and when 26 years old was employed as a skilled craftsman in Edinburgh. In the year 1782 he journeyed to London and worked as a mason on Somerset House, then in course of erection, but after two years he went to Portsmouth to superintend the erection of buildings for the Commissioner at Portsmouth Dockyard. In 1787 he accepted an appointment at Shrewsbury on extensive undertakings in connexion with estates, and soon afterwards both the County Authority of Shropshire and the Borough engaged him to make surveys and designs for important works. His services were not for long, however, circumscribed by the boundaries of one county, and his talents were employed in the design and execution of great bridges, canals, water works, harbours, docks, and many important highways. He was the first president of the Institution of Civil Engineers.

JOHN LOUDON McADAM

In the year 1827 the Government, during the short period of Canning's premiership, offered to John Loudon McAdam a baronetcy for his services in the cause to which he had devoted his life, and which had resulted in so marked an improvement in the methods of road making. The honour was declined, possibly in consequence of his age (he was then 71), and his inadequate means, but it is interesting to record that during his lifetime a knighthood was conferred upon his third surviving son, James Nicoll McAdam, of Tindon End, Essex, in 1834, by William IV, out of compliment to his father, who was in those days styled " The Great Improver of British Roads."

MODERN ROAD HISTORY

The second epoch in modern road history dates from the year 1878, when the Highways and Locomotive (Amendment) Act, came into operation. This marked the end of the turnpike era. In the year 1882, the State, for the first time, recognized that it had to shoulder some responsibility for the maintenance of the highways of the country, and voted the sum of £250,000. In 1888, the passing of the

Local Government Act marked the next forward step by creating the County Councils, and delegating to them the duty of maintaining the main roads. The Act of 1894, which made the Rural District Councils the authorities for the roads within their own areas, completed the administrative organization.

The setting up of the Road Board in 1910 introduced a new feature into the scheme of road control, the final result of which cannot be foreseen. This Board came into existence under the powers which were conferred for its constitution by the Development and Road Improvement Funds Act of 1909. The setting up of this Central Authority has been fruitful of much good, and in 1919 it was merged in the newly-created Ministry of Transport.

Many, who were on the active list as Road Surveyors, carried the traditions of the second era in the history of modern road construction into the third important epoch, which followed the peace of 1918. The Great War expanded our ideas on the subject of roads, made us realize what an important part they play in the affairs of men, and taught us much about methods of construction. Mechanical road transport was perfected by the demands of war, its sphere of useful operations considerably enlarged, and its possibilities so clearly emphasized that the death knell of all previous methods was tolled.

Although our modern roads can be regarded as one of the greatest triumphs of Western civilization, it is remarkable how scant is the public knowledge of the subject, and this book is intended to throw some light on this most interesting topic of Road Making and Road Using.

CHAPTER II

THE ROAD MAKER

WHEN we speak or write of the famous engineers who constructed our wonderful bridges, we think of them as "Bridge builders"; and in the same way, when we have in mind the engineers who are engaged upon the building of our important highways, we use the term "Road makers."

The evolution of the road engineer—the road maker—from his early prototype has been gradual. In 1718, William Nelson published his book on *The Office and Authority of Surveyors of Highways*. These officers, like their successors in title, had multifarious duties to perform. They had, however, to deal with infectious persons, diseased meat, and other matters classified as "Nuisances," which seem to have had pre-eminence of road construction works. The surveyor had to see to the scouring of ditches, and should the persons responsible for this operation "lay the soil in the highway and suffer it to be there six months they forfeit twelve pence per load." By the Statute of the Fifth of Elizabeth, surveyors were vested with powers relating to the free passage of water from roadways, and proper flows in the ditches, from which it is evident that either the roads were made of earth or the destructive effect of water in the structure was known. But the most interesting item relates to the method of administration. In those days "the Surveyor must give publick notice from time to time every four months what defaults he finds, this Notice to be given in the Parish Church the next Sunday after Sermon ended." At that time the appointment to the office of surveyor was made as follows: "Two Tradesmen must be chosen by the Constables . . . on Monday and Tuesday in Easter week yearly to be Surveyors of the Highway."

COUNTY SURVEYOR

That road construction could be reduced to an exact science had never been fully recognized before 1819, but in that year, in the Report of the Select Committee, the term "Science of Road Making" became established; and from that time we can trace the improved status of those entrusted with road works. To enable a system of larger, though decentralized, control of roads to be established, it was at the same time, in 1819, recommended that each county should appoint an executive officer as a "County Surveyor," "whose services should be amply remunerated, as only persons of superior ability" were to be considered suitable for such positions. The principle of county responsibility, however, can be traced back to the reign of Henry VIII, when it was enacted that all bridges and highways, for a distance of 300 yards, on each side of such bridges, should, as a general rule, be a charge on the county. A further recommendation was also made in 1819, which aimed at the efficient training of engineers in the science of road making. Although since that time much has been done in this direction, much remains to be accomplished.

CHAIR OF HIGHWAY ENGINEERING

The Chair of Highway Engineering, established in 1928, at the London University, was a step in the right direction. During the first two decades of the last century, much information was collected by Select Committees of the House of Commons on the general subject of road construction, maintenance, and administration. John Loudon McAdam was, during that period, reaching the zenith of his fame as a road maker. He wrote extensively on the subject, and the following are excerpts from his published works—

" Will it be deemed presumptuous to propose that some regulations may be adopted for encouraging and promoting a better system of making roads, by eliciting the exertion of science, of creating a set of officers of skill and reputation to superintend this most essential branch of domestic economy."

" Much must depend on the selection of the officers . . . . the subject of road making ought to have been well considered by him ; his station in society should be such as to secure him . . . . . obedience . . . . . of the subordinate officers."

"The application of scientific principles which has hitherto never been thought of would remedy the evil," the "evil" being "the present bad condition of the roads."

" The want of science in the surveyor has gone hand in hand with improvident expenditure."

" The duties of a head surveyor demand suitable education and talents."

" The success of this plan of appointing county surveyors will, in a degree, depend upon . . . . . . integrity, talents, and energy of character . . . . some skill in the science of an engineer."

" If the House shall approve the formation of a Board of Commissioners they will deem it proper to place at its head some person of eminent station and character, as a security for the independence and respectability of its proceedings."

" Abuses can only be put down by officers in the situation of gentlemen."

" I think the defect lies in the want of science in road making."

" The want of this scientific system leads . . . . . . to a great waste of public money."

MORE THAN 100 YEARS AGO

When it is borne in mind that these opinions were expressed more than 100 years ago, the prophetic vision, clear thinking, fearless outspoken words and activities of McAdam, ought to entitle him to a high place in the ranks of our really great men. In noting the development of the science of road making from such unpromising conditions as existed 100 years ago, it is possible to trace the evolution of the road maker. It seems hardly credible that at the time of McAdam the subject of road making was so little understood, that the most unsuitable persons were appointed surveyors of roads, and regarded, whilst holding their positions, with complacency. Nepotism flourished at the expense of efficiency.

TO-DAY

To-day the holders of such positions have to be trained men of superior attainments, and the modern highways are a striking testimony to their capacity and skill. Most of these men who have charge of this important national and local asset—the roads—are highly qualified Civil Engineers. In their ranks are to be found those who, regardless of criticism and abuse, have, by their conduct, and the certainty of their own opinions, done so much to introduce new ideas and methods of road construction. McAdam was laughed at, abused, and jeered; those who supported him were, for a long time, nicknamed "Macadamites," but he won through and lived long enough to have his services fully appreciated. The road maker of to-day, in like manner, has come into his own.

But the road engineer, who, in accordance with the fitness of things it seems proper to call the road maker, has recognized that he cannot alone solve the problems which, until the last century, were thought by most people to be soluble by means of brawn without brains, and with tools and materials without the application of scientific principles. The chemist is now closely associated with the engineer, and chemistry and physics are being more and more applied in the development of the modern highway. Nothing is more indicative of the changed conditions in industry than the activities of the Department of Scientific and Industrial Research, which has a Road Research branch, and the National Physical Laboratory. No longer can laboratory research work be regarded as academic and of little practical importance, as results are daily proving just the opposite.

PART II: DESIGN IN ROAD MAKING

CHAPTER III

DESIGN

SINCE the days of the Romans no one, until such men as Wade and Telford arose, had realized that design was essential in the layout and construction of the highways, but in recent years, the subject has been more seriously entertained than ever before. Because of failure in the past to do so we recognize the importance of design as we are to-day faced with the problems of the insufficient, narrow, tortuous, though picturesque highways of this country. These old roads, which have developed through long years of slow-moving horse-drawn traffic, have suddenly been required to deal with heavy high speed self-propelled vehicles, the antitheses of everything that was in the minds of our immediate predecessors. So serious, from the engineering, financial, and often archaeological point of view has this subject become, that it is often found to be much more advantageous to lay out a new road along a brand new alignment, than to attempt to improve an existing one. For this reason the many new arterial, by-pass, and orbital roads, about which so much is heard these days, have come or are coming into being. Design is now playing an important part, and the centralization of authority in an expert body, known as the Ministry of Transport, is co-ordinating the work of the numerous highway authorities of the kingdom. and bringing all their schemes into line with each other—or at least endeavouring to do so.

TRAFFIC CENSUS

The traffic demands of the present time can always be ascertained by a census of vehicles. In compiling this information, it is necessary to have a clear conception of

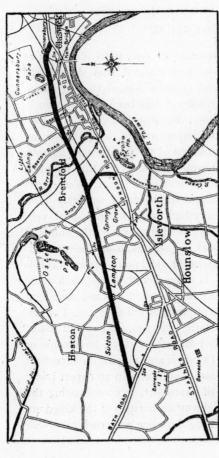

THE GREAT WEST ROAD: THE ALIGNMENT

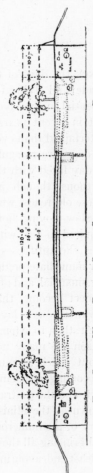

THE GREAT WEST ROAD: CROSS SECTION FOR 120-FOOT ROAD
From *Notes on the Great West Road*, by Mr. A. Dyland, late County Surveyor of Middlesex

THE GREAT WEST ROAD: AERIAL PHOTOGRAPH

the subject. It may be interesting to know the number of vehicles passing over a certain section of any road per day, but for the road maker, who has to design the foundations and wearing surface, much more data will be required. It is better to know the tonnage per yard width of roadway, as some narrow roads have to carry loads as heavy, if not heavier than others of greater width. In this calculation, a factor of safety is provided if three feet is deducted from the actual width of the carriageway, as the bulk of the traffic, in passing up and down, keeps 18 inches from each edge of the road. A water bound road, having a width of 20 feet, should, if properly constructed, be able to carry 500 tons per day ; but a road of the same width should carry four times that volume of traffic, without deformation, if made of a suitable bituminous bound macadam. Traffic intensity is a most difficult problem to solve. With the information which a census return will afford, it is always the local knowledge of circumstances which makes the deciding factors in the design for construction purposes. Theoretically it ought to be possible to standardize roads to traffic conditions, but it cannot be done, because of the difficulty, amongst others, of differentiating between up and down traffic, which may vary very considerably in both weight and speed. This applies, of course, more particularly to industrial areas.

PROVIDING FOR HEAVY " THROUGH TRAFFIC "

If called upon to decide what type of road will be most serviceable, it is advisable, in addition to the collected data and local information, to seek out a road where similar conditions exist, and compare notes, before making a final decision. The road maker has little control over the vehicles which use the roads for which he is responsible. In the days which antedated the introduction of the self-propelled vehicle, road traffic was chiefly local in character, and of a slow-moving description. To-day a large percentage of the traffic may be what is termed " through " ;

and may be reckoned as coming into the category of " heavy." This factor must not be overlooked in designing a road, for the chances are that as soon as a road has been made, or an old one improved or reconstructed, through traffic will make use of it.

A knowledge of local topography may enable existing roads to be altered to relieve the overburdened ones, and this can sometimes be achieved by obtaining powers to convert certain roads into one-way traffic routes, and thus make certain of ensuring greater freedom of movement for vehicles.

One of the most important features in the design of a road is the careful planning of junctions, so that other roads come in at correct angles without steep gradients. If a right-angled junction cannot be provided, the intersecting road must be widened out on each side for some distance, and a radius of not less than 50 feet provided. In every case it ought to be possible for an uninterrupted view to be obtained by the driver of every vehicle before entering upon the road. Where possible, a " Circus " plan should be adopted so that all traffic is compelled to gyrate.

VISIBILITY AND ALIGNMENT

In consequence of the intensive use of the roads by fast-moving traffic, visibility has become a first essential if loss of life is to be avoided. Granted sufficient visibility, the speed of any vehicle on any road should never exceed the capacity of the mechanical means to bring such vehicle to rest within a distance of 50 yards. No vehicle ought to travel on any road, where a clear vision of 100 yards is not attainable, at a higher speed than 20 miles per hour. The road maker's responsibility in this direction is very onerous, and as he is now armed with sufficient powers, he ought to insist upon the removal of all hedges, banks, trees, hoardings, and even buildings, where the minimum visibility does not exist to ensure adequate safety.

Alignment and directness of route are as necessary to-day

The Great West Road: Ribbon Development and Dual Carriageway

as in the time of the Romans, but physical conditions have to be considered, and in avoiding steep gradients, detours must be made. When this becomes necessary it is essential that long sweeping curves shall be provided, and that no such curve shall have a less radius than 500 feet.

LOCAL GEOLOGY

A knowledge of the geology of the district is important for the successful execution of road works. Where a road has to be carried around a hill, the site has to be very carefully prospected, and the inclination of the strata ascertained. If the laminations are parallel with the road surface, much trouble may ensue from the slipping or sliding of the strata, which may entail very expensive operations. A thorough acquaintance with the geological formation of the district may result in the successful utilization of local materials, and, in consequence, a considerable economy in the cost of the work.

ROADS AND RAILWAYS

Co-operation between the highway and railway authorities, though hardly a subject which falls strictly within the purview of this book, should not be overlooked. In the layout of a proposed road, the contiguity, or otherwise, of a railway system is a point to be kept in view. It may happen that in the near future, when more harmonious relationships exist between the two systems—road and rail—that the burden of work will be more advantageously distributed ; therefore it is not a wise policy, at the moment, to design a road parallel with, and contiguous to an existing railway. Roads as feeders for railways should always be considered, roads in districts distant from railways are vital, and roads which cross railways may be regarded as necessary owing to the opposite direction in which they run.

Co-operation and co-ordination are matters which should be kept to the fore between authorities who are active with town or regional planning schemes. In consequence

CIRCUS AT JUNCTION OF WATFORD BY-PASS AND NORTH CIRCULAR ROAD, BRENT

(Photo: Tecart Studios, London, W.C.1)

of the rapidly changing conditions, it is no longer possible for any local authority, in this densely populated country, to assume an attitude of aloofness, for its roads are the inalienable birthright of the most distant inhabitant. Adjoining authorities should move, in all their projects, in harmony with each other, and, in this way, safeguard the next generation from the difficulties which beset us to-day in dealing with this problem of roads.

ESSENTIALS IN ROAD DESIGN

To enable a grasp of the essentials of modern road construction to be obtained, the following are the ideals, or the aims to be kept in view by the road maker, in the design of new roads, or of schemes for the betterment of existing highways.—

1. Good alignment, directness, and visibility.
2. Easy gradients.
3. Correct cambers.
4. Sufficient width.
5. Properly designed curves.
6 Freedom from blind corners.
7. Adequate underdrainage.
8. A stable subsoil, either natural or prepared, to carry the foundation.
9. An adequate foundation.
10. A surface suitable for the general character of the traffic, which will vary according to geographical, physical, industrial, and residential conditions.
11. Economical construction with efficiency.
12. Safety for pedestrians.
13. Intelligently placed signs and direction posts.
14. Co-ordination of two or more authorities, and with the local planning authorities.
15. Sufficient and efficient lighting.
16. Tree planting.
17. Cycle tracks.

A "Vista Road"—Churchfields, Broxbourne, Herts

(*Photo: Tecart Studios, London, W.C.1*)

In addition to the physical conditions which control the design of roads in its engineering aspects, there has to be borne in mind the clamant demand for amenities. Of these the subject of "Ribbon Development" is by far the most important, as the object of those who have been active in securing legislation is both for the preservation of the beauty of the open road and the safety of those who use it, whether afoot or awheel.

In the design of important roads in the future, it is certain that they will have to be considered more as an architectural feature than has been the case in the past. During recent decades, the utilitarian has alone or at least chiefly been considered in the layout of roads, with the result that the approaches to our towns are invariably sordid and drab; indeed, many environs are squalid.

In this connexion the two types of road, the inter-urban for communication within the town's environs, and the road which links up the towns through which it passes directly or by means of by-passes, will each require separate and distinct treatment.

A reminder of old-time city security can be obtained by either the erection of a gateway or other properly-designed structure at the boundary of a town, or at the point where the transition from urban to rural is abrupt.

In the years prior to 1939 the newspapers devoted much attention to the subject of the preservation of England's beauty spots, which, it was declared, were being "uglified" by the removal of glorious old trees and other irreplaceable relics from the past, to enable roads to be built or, as it was termed, "improved."

These roads were, it was alleged, driven through areas where, by a slight deviation of alignment, much that was beautiful could have been saved for the edification and delight of future generations. Road engineers in future will have to work in much closer co-operation with the architect and landscape gardener than they have done in the past.

AMENITIES

John Citizen is not devoid of sentiment. If such were the case we should never hear of the movements which aim at maintaining the beauty of the highways. In an age such as ours, when so very often ideals have to be pushed aside for the utilitarian, it is good to know that efforts are being made to co-ordinate the aesthetic with the practical and commercial in the construction of new roads. This is as it should be, for we have an heritage of beauty in our old highways, and we must show our appreciation of the efforts made for us by our predecessors, and co-operate by taking steps to provide for the generations as yet unborn. By modern legislation, the Highway Authorities have been given extended powers for the planting and guarding of trees and shrubs alongside the roads. It could, of course, be argued that, owing to the fickleness of our climate, there is not that same necessity for roadside trees as one experiences in the more sunny countries of the world, but the contrast between the bare gauntness of the modern road—that is the road on a new alignment—and the older tree-fringed highways of this country will compel the hearty co-operation of all parties in the work of tree planting and the beautifying of all new highways. The continuous lines of poles, which carry the telephone and telegraph lines over the length and breadth of this country, do not add a charm to the scenery (unless *stately* uniformity can be so regarded). The multiplicity of wires very often compels the mutilation of trees, which is to be regretted. Efforts should be made to put all these wires underground. Here is a chance for the close co-operation of Government with the local authorities.

Street hoardings have become picture galleries, and, when used to hide decayed buildings or dumping grounds, they receive a benediction; but, when erected along our glorious old highways, shutting out the scenery or being a blot on the landscape at some beauty spot, we have a grievance against the vendors of pills, soaps, milks, cosmetics and other commodities, and would ask these people

to co-operate with, and not work against, us in our efforts to
maintain the beauties, decencies, and quiet respectabilities
which have always been regarded as one of our national
characteristics.

Owners of land could do much to co-operate with others
in making more of vistas than is now done.   The vista is
a much neglected source of beauty in this country.

CHAPTER IV

GRADIENTS, CAMBER, WIDTHS, ABUTMENTS

IN consequence of the generally ample reserve of power, which is a feature of the self-propelled vehicle, and the improvements in the braking mechanism, the question of gradients is not so serious a matter as formerly. Horse transport will continue for some time to come, and must be considered when designing any road. On economic grounds however, whether we are thinking in terms of mechanical traffic or horse drawn vehicles, the flatter the gradient the better for all interests concerned, as the additional cost per ton foot of rise becomes a recognized factor in computing haulage expenses. In this connexion, as in practically all the points to be considered in the study of this subject of roads and vehicles, it is the local conditions which are important. The maximum grade will be governed by the class of traffic that is expected to use the road, and like the parallel case of the weakest link in the chain, it must be designed to enable the lowest-powered vehicle to traverse its length with the minimum of tractive effort. The character of the road surface will be controlled by the gradient, local conditions, and the amount of money available for the work. Gradient is a longitudinal slope, and is defined as the proportion between length and difference in height of its extreme points. If a road rises one foot in every 50 feet of its length, its gradient is 1 in 50, or what is termed a 2 per cent grade. Resistance, due to the action of gravity on any incline in pounds per ton of vehicle weight, is equal to 2,200/rate of grade.

PROVISION FOR HORSE-DRAWN TRAFFIC

As the horse is the weakest tractive agent for hauling vehicles, gradients must be designed to come within that animal's draught capacity. An average horse, travelling at a speed of 3 miles per hour, can exert a force of 100 to 125 pounds on a smooth level road. This power diminishes with increase of speed in inverse proportion to it. From a series of tests that have been made over working days of 10 hours' duration, it has been ascertained that the tractive capacity of a horse is doubled when only 5 hours' work is done per day. On inclines the draught capacity of a horse rapidly diminishes, as so much energy is expended in overcoming the resistance of gravity and road surface. Foothold for horses is an important factor, and the smoother the surface the flatter must be the gradient. Fatigue, due to effort, cannot be calculated theoretically, but is an important item in reducing the working power of a horse. It does not, of course, enter into the consideration of the subject when self-propelled vehicles are concerned. During the winter months, or when the roads are slippery, from any cause whatever, the seriousness of steep gradients becomes all the more apparent.

Prior to the introduction of self-propelled vehicles, it was recognized that the following gradients should not be exceeded—

| Soft wood paving | . | 1 in 20 | Asphalt | . | 1 in 60 |
| | Water bound macadam | . | 1 in 30 | | |

A horse that can draw one ton on the level can move the following loads as the gradients become steeper.

| 1 in 50 | . | 0·80 of a ton | 1 in 20 | . | 0·40 of a ton |
| 1 in 40 | . | 0·70 ,, ,, | 1 in 10 | . | 0·25 ,, ,, |

SAFE LIMITS

In recent years it has been found possible to construct roads with steeper gradients, but for impervious surfaces a slope of 1 in 15 should not be exceeded, the same for granite setts. Yorkshire or Lancashire soft grit stone setts afford a good foothold for horses on steep grades. Bituminous road surfaces, with carefully graded coarse clinker aggregates and low penetration bitumen as a binder, have been used on gradients as steep as 1 in 10. A gradient of

1 in 25 may be considered to meet modern traffic needs, though 1 in 30 should be regarded as a ruling gradient.   On all grades every effort should be made to reduce the length and to flatten it as frequently as possible.   On steep grades it is essential that sharp curves should be avoided ; and no acute apex point, where two gradients meet, should be permitted.   At such a place the approaches on each side should be eased to allow of not less than 50 yards of vision, as there is a distinct element of danger in the approach of two vehicles when out of sight of each other.

The minimum longitudinal slope of a road is 1 in 250, which is sufficient to drain off storm water.   When this cannot be provided by the available fall in the road it is necessary to lower the gully gratings to provide for the flow in the channels.

CAMBER

In so simple a matter as the camber, cross section or convexity of a road, the rule of thumb method has persisted down to very recent times, and in this fact can be traced the long arm of custom.   In the days prior to the introduction of the steam road roller, this roundness was styled " barrelling."   McAdam, who had strong and sound views on most subjects connected with road construction, and was emphatic on this, was always objecting to the excessive crown of the roads.   In those days it was the custom to heap up the broken stones in the middle of the road.   The vehicles pressed some of them down and scattered the remainder.   Men, employed for the purpose, kept raking the loose material always towards the centre of the road, which resulted in excessive cambering. Again, in more recent times, the renewal of roads simply meant the application of another coat of stone to the old surface. In this way, although a substantial wearing crust was formed, the camber became too high.   A serious objection to an excessive camber is to be found in the fact that the traffic must keep to the centre of the road, and always run in the same tracks, which results in unequal road wear, and excessive maintenance costs. Prior to the introduction of impervious road surfaces, camber was also allowed to develop, as it was regarded as being advantageous for rapidly draining off storm water into the channels. Camber, on the other hand, must not be so flat that the surface wear of the road, or slight hollows in any part, will allow water to stand in pools. Not only is this unsightly, unhealthy, and disagreeable, by reason of the splashing by the wheels of vehicles, but it may allow water to percolate through to the foundation, and weaken the structure.

In the resurfacing of a road, it is much better, when levels permit, to raise the sides rather than lower the centre. In this way the expense of refixing kerbs and channels may be more than compensated for by the substantial undisturbed old road crust, which could not be replaced by any foundation of equal value, except at a high cost. As the weakest part of a road is often at the haunches (the third part of the width on each side from channels), this method has much to be said in its favour.

Road makers have, at various times, adopted different types of camber or profile for their roads, and in no case has this been a true arc of a circle ; consequently when camber is referred to, as though it were graded, it differs considerably from the longitudinal grade or slope of a road, as it presents in cross section a slight convexity.[1]

Owing to the great increase in the intensity and speed of traffic the former ideas about camber have changed; and as the materials employed in road construction have so much improved an excessive cross fall, which is no longer allowed, may easily be avoided. For dense and homogeneous

[1] In order to ascertain the correct camber, or for setting out a road at actual site of work, the following formula will be found useful. Decide the height of the centre of the road above or below the kerb, as may be required, then divide distance from kerb to centre into four equal parts. Let the height from an imaginary base line at channel level, at centre of road, equal $1 \cdot 0$, then towards the kerb the perpendiculars will be $0 \cdot 87$, $0 \cdot 65$, $0 \cdot 35$.

surfaces, flat cross falls only are needed, as water easily flows off; and owing to their impervious characteristics, the foundations of such a road are unaffected by water. Because of this, and as a minimum cross fall only is required, the camber may be formed of a straight slope from each channel meeting at an angular intersection at the centre of the road. But as such a shape at the centre would be undesirable the central portion, about a third of the whole width, must be rounded off with a curve tangential to the side slopes.

APPROXIMATE CAMBERS

Longitudinal slope has a distinct bearing on this question of camber, or cross fall, as on a slight gradient all the surface water must flow into the channels at a right angle with the central axis of the road, and not along the road surface ; hence the flatter the grade the greater must be the camber or cross section of the road.

The approximate cambers for the various methods of road surfacing may be taken as—

Water bound macadam . . .	1 in 25 to 1 in 30
Water bound macadam, but tar sprayed	1 in 35
Tar macadam	1 in 35 to 1 in 40
Bituminous, sealed surface, asphalt, concrete, wood blocks, granite setts	1 in 40 to 1 in 50

SUPER-ELEVATION

From these figures it will be seen that the smoother the road and the less permeable the surface the flatter the camber should be made. For the modern high speed rubber-tyred vehicles, it is necessary to reduce the chances of side slipping. At places where quick or short length curves occur, it is advisable to reduce the overturning moments, because of the centrifugal force of vehicles when moving round such curves. To obtain this a gradual change of formation from camber to a cross fall of $\frac{1}{2}$ to $\frac{3}{4}$ inch to each foot of width, is required.

Owing, however, to the varying degrees of speed at which the many types of road vehicles travel, and the different kinds of road surfacings, and changeable weather conditions, it is not always easy to calculate what the super-elevation should be. For all curves with a radius not exceeding 1000 feet a reasonable super-elevation should, when possible, be provided.

Where curves to secure change from a horizontal direction have to be made, they should be as gradual as possible.

CONCAVE ROAD

It has been suggested that roads concave in cross section would be better than those as at present constructed with convex profiles. Such a method of construction, though it would partially solve the problem of super elevation, would introduce the problem of how best to dispose of the storm water from such an inverted form of road surface.

WIDTHS

When speaking or writing about roads, we frequently make use of the words "sufficient" and "commodious." A road must be of sufficient capacity for the demands of the traffic, and commodious enough to satisfy the requirements of the users, who are of two classes—one of which is the pedestrian. The question of road width is a most perplexing one, and the opinions of road makers have been at variance on this subject. If it were possible to foresee what the road traffic may be in 50 years' time, the problem would be easier of solution. But, there is much to be said in favour of the wide road, as should traffic demands increase, the wide road will make dual carriageways possible. On the other hand, if the extreme width of road is not required for traffic purposes, the open spaces will be valuable as boulevards, and for the perflation of air.

Our old, narrow, tortuous roads, are survivals of the slow-going days, and their picturesqueness endears them to us; but they are veritable death-traps. It would, possibly, be correct to say that the average width of these important old roads does not exceed 15 to 18 feet.

WIDTH AND PURPOSE

In considering this question of road width, it is necessary to keep clearly in mind the purposes for which any particular road will be required. The model by-laws of the old Local Government Board required a residential street to be 36 feet wide, and the footpaths to be each $\frac{1}{6}$ of the entire width. But this rule does not apply to through communication roads, the width of which must vary, as circumstances demand, from 80 to 120 feet, or more. It is necessary to avoid extremes, for a road of excessive width may be as objectionable as one too narrow, and, on aesthetic grounds, much more so. An excessively wide road entails considerable first cost in construction, and a more than reasonable expense in maintenance. A wide road presents more dangers for the pedestrian in crossing than a narrow one, as on such a road the speed fiend finds his greatest delight. In foggy weather a wide road may become very dangerous, as at such times the kerbs are the only guides for drivers, and the farther away from them the greater the danger becomes.

Again, many of the present-day road surfaces, and particularly bituminous ones, require that the whole surface shall be in constant use. Continual traffic has an ironing out effect, keeping the surface free from wheel tracks, and preventing disintegration. Degeneration of the materials of which such a road surface is composed, may be akin to the atrophy by disuse with which we are acquainted in nature.

It has been decided that the wider roads should be divided up into two parts to enable vehicles to move in a continuous stream, each in the same direction, one portion of the road for "up" and the other for "down" traffic. A central boulevard strip is possible for a road having an overall width of 120 feet. With such an arrangement it may be necessary to restrict the minimum and not the maximum speed of vehicles, provided it is possible to avoid the dangers of road junctions.

WESTERN AVENUE, MIDDLESEX, SHOWING DIVIDED ROAD AND
SIDE BAY
(Photo: Tecart Studios, London, W.C.1)

STANDARD WIDTHS

This reference to the width of roads is incomplete without stating the Ministry of Transport's former rule, viz. that the standard or multiple width for carriageways should be 10 feet, that is to say, for two lines of traffic the carriageway must be 20 feet, and for three 30 feet wide. Further, that for the more populous parts of the United Kingdom, and as a general policy for the guidance of road makers, the following standard might be observed—

Width of carriageway	30 feet
Two footpaths of 8 feet width each . . .	16 ,,
Two verges, each 7 feet wide	14 ,,
Total width between fences . . .	60 feet

The Circular, however, which was addressed by the Ministry of Transport to the highway authorities throughout England, Wales, and Scotland in March, 1946, has modified these old standards. The Minister, after consideration, has reached the following conclusions—

(a) The unit width for each lane of traffic should be 10 feet. In a road, the carriageway of which comprises not more than two traffic lanes but is likely to carry a large proportion of industrial vehicles of maximum dimensions, the unit width should generally be increased to 11 feet.

(b) Where an existing road carries, or a proposed road is expected to carry, 400 vehicles at the peak hour, dual carriageways will be desirable. In any case where more than two traffic lanes may be necessary, dual carriageways should, where practicable, be provided in preference to widening the single carriageways. Dual carriageways will often be justified solely on grounds of public safety. (In calculating the total number of vehicles, two pedal cycles may be regarded as equivalent to one vehicle.)

(c) The standard widths adopted should provide for such future widening of the carriageways, together with

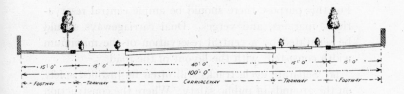

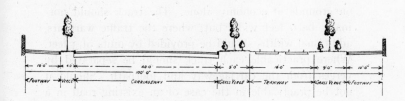

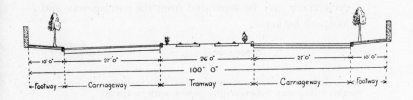

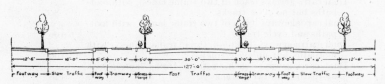

FOUR CROSS SECTIONS SHOWING HOW IT IS POSSIBLE
TO DIVIDE A ROADWAY INTO PARTS

From a paper entitled "The Evolution of the Road and Transport thereon" by Mr.
F. Marsden, City Engineer and Surveyor of Bradford, at a conference of the Municipal
and County Engineers in London on the 29th Nov., 1923.

Compare the above with the Ministry of Transport's 1946 publication: *Design and
Layout of Roads in Built-up Areas.*

cycle tracks and footpaths, as may become necessary. For this purpose there should be ample central reservations, margins, and verges. Dual carriageways should be separated by a central reservation of the maximum width consistent with the layout of the road.

(*d*) Separate cycle tracks will often be justified solely on the grounds of public safety. Where the construction of cycle tracks will avoid the necessity for widening an existing carriageway, their provision may be justified on grounds of economy alone. The track should normally be 6 feet wide, but, where the traffic warrants, additional widths should be provided by units of 3 feet. Where practicable each track should be separated by verges from the carriageway and footpath. Should it not be practicable in the case of an existing road in a built-up area to obtain sufficient space for verges, the cycle track may be separated from the carriageway and footpath by kerbs.

Proposed layout	Minimum Standard Width to be adopted
	ft.
Single carriageway not exceeding 30 feet, with footpaths	60
Single carriageway not exceeding 30 feet, with footpaths and cycle tracks	80
Dual carriageways (each of two traffic lanes), with footpaths but no cycle tracks	80
Dual carriageways (each of two traffic lanes), with footpaths and cycle tracks	100
Dual carriageways (each of three traffic lanes), with footpaths but no cycle tracks	100
Dual carriageways (each of three traffic lanes), with footpaths and cycle tracks	120
Further provision for wider cycle tracks, additional width of verges for improved visibility or equestrian traffic, greater space for services of improved amenities as required.	

Where it is apparent that a section of the road as ultimately to be developed will be on an embankment or in a cutting, the standard width for the section should be increased by one or more 20 feet units to embrace the sites of the slopes. It may be convenient to refer to this as the

"*extended standard width*" as distinguished from the ordinary
"standard width" required for the particular type of layout
selected.

ABUTMENTS

A cambered road has been likened to an arch, but this
simile can only be made to apply where substantial
abutments, such as kerbs and channels, exist, where the
camber is high, and the crust is of a compact homogeneous
mass. An old well consolidated water bound macadam
road will sometimes meet this requirement ; where a road
is paved with wood blocks or granite setts, or constructed
of concrete, when sufficient abutments exist, the principles
of the arch might be applied. Traffic stresses, though
they may be in a longitudinal direction, are distributed over
a considerable area, and as there is far less resistance on a
road unprovided with abutments, such as a kerb or edging,
there is always a tendency for the materials, of which the
road is formed, to creep away in a lateral direction.

PURPOSE OF THE KERB

The type of abutment or kerb ought to be made to
vary with the width of the road and the character of
the traffic to be borne. On a narrow road the traffic
is more intensified; consequently a deeper kerb is necessary, because the traffic travels nearer the kerb. In
addition to preventing the lateral movement, or creep of
road-making materials, a kerb is necessary as an abutment
for tar, bituminous macadam, for asphalt, or any form of
mastic carpeting, and for granite setts or wood block
paving. It prevents vehicles from encroaching on the
portions of a road that are allotted for the use of pedestrians,
and is, therefore, a safety provision. Kerbs on roadways
in urban districts are also required to form the side of the
channel to conduct surface water towards the inlets to the
sewers. A street kerb should be deep enough to withstand
the lateral thrust of the traffic, and strong enough to resist

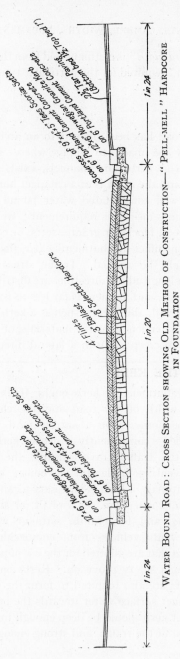

WATER BOUND ROAD : CROSS SECTION SHOWING OLD METHOD OF CONSTRUCTION—"PELL-MELL" HARDCORE
IN FOUNDATION

Note vertical and horizontal joints

12"x6" Norwegian Granite Kerb
3 courses of 9"x4½"x5" Tees Scoria Concrete
on 6" Portland Cement Concrete

3 courses of 9"x4½"x5" Tees Scoria Concrete
on 6" Portland Cement Concrete
12"x6" Norwegian Granite Kerb

2½" Tar Paving Granite Concrete
(Bottom bed 1½", Top bed 1")

3" Selected Hardcore

3" Ballast

4" Flints

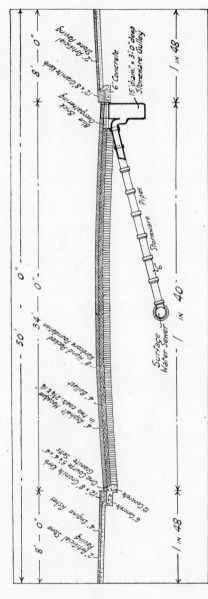

CROSS SECTION SHOWING HAND PACKED METHOD OF CONSTRUCTING FOUNDATION

Note all the joints are vertical—asphalt wearing coat

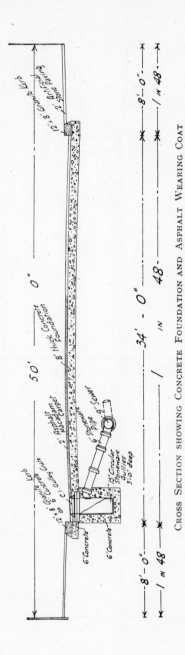

CROSS SECTION SHOWING CONCRETE FOUNDATION AND ASPHALT WEARING COAT

the abrasive action of wheels. If it is insufficient in cubic content, deformation will quickly ensue, due to overturning movements.

KINDS OF KERB

Kerbs are generally formed of granite, sandstone, limestone, brick, or concrete, the last named being either precast or made *in situ*. For streets with heavy traffic, granite is the most serviceable material. Its cost varies according to the dressing or the amount of labour which the mason has bestowed upon it and not with the quality of the stone. These kerb-stones may be either carefully chisel dressed or only hammer faced. Superior types of chisel cut stones can be obtained, but in all qualities it is essential that the ends should be clean and square cut, to ensure a neat butt joint. For streets with light traffic, blue brick, concrete, or stone, other than granite, can be used. In the heavier types of granite kerb, no piece should be less than 3 feet long, and the other dimensions are generally 6 inches wide, and 12 inches deep. It is open to serious doubt whether, under present-day conditions, this standard depth of 12 inches is sufficient ; 16 inches would be much better. Such a size would provide for 12 inches to be placed below the road level, to act as an abutment against lateral pressure, and 4 inches to demarcate the carriageway and provide a barrier against traffic encroachment on to the footways; or as an alternative to using larger kerbs the thickness or depth of the concrete may be increased to provide the extra abutment which present-day traffic conditions demand. Sometimes this class of granite kerb is laid flat, and although it has a bold appearance it is useless as an abutment. All kerbs should be laid on a bed of concrete at least 6 inches thick, and the concrete should be extended behind the kerb to half its total depth. In order to secure stability, where channels are laid in conjunction with kerbs, either in granite, stone, or concrete, the bed should be laid for both kerb and channel in one operation, when the longitudinal fall of the kerb coincides with that of the channel.

In the Memorandum No. 575 on the Layout and Construction of Roads, the Ministry of War Transport laid down that—

(1) Kerbs should always be provided in built-up areas, over bridges, and at the foot of any retaining wall which may abut on a carriageway.

(2) Regard to be had to the advisability of using local materials.

(3) In open country the use of roughly-dressed stone is considered appropriate; or where a raised kerb is not required, a sunken kerb, in conjunction with grass-edging, is recommended.

(4) Sharp arrises to kerbs to be avoided—a chamfer from the vertical, rounded section, or splayed front edge is recommended.

(5) The height of kerbs should, it is suggested, be—

(*a*) In built-up areas, 3 to 5 inches.

(*b*) In rural areas, 4 inches.

(*c*) For cycle tracks (kerb not always required), $1\frac{1}{2}$ inches.

PRECAST CONCRETE KERBS

Precast concrete kerbs can be made to have a most pleasing appearance, but they do not retain this attribute under the abrasive action of traffic. In the manufacture of this class of kerb, the aggregates of granite should range from $\frac{3}{4}$ to $\frac{3}{8}$ inch in size ; the sand should be clean, and as the product should be as voidless as possible, the proportions should be 3 granite, $1\frac{1}{2}$ sand, and 1 Portland cement. The moulds should be of steel, and the filling performed on rocking tables, to ensure the maximum density.

Density, in the manufacture of this class of material, can be secured by the use of machinery for pressing the blocks, which ensures the expulsion of surplus water, and the more perfect crystallization of the cement. Only the minimum quantity of water should be used in the mixing of the materials. The casting of a concrete kerb *in situ* is not to be recommended, as it is impossible to secure either the density or finish which is required for this class of work. Unless very special conditions prevail, it will be found to be more advantageous to lay precast concrete kerbs than to make use of the materials for this purpose *in situ*. Concrete kerbs should be formed either with a half-round nosing, a chamfered or bevelled edge, or a face splayed from the channel, or a combination of these, to offer fewer chances of damage by wheels. The face of the kerb should never be vertical from the channel. The back of the kerb, next to the footpath, should be straight throughout its entire depth, and the full thickness should be continued from the base to the channel or road level. On slopes a concrete edging was useless, as road kerbs were used for the braking of vehicles ; and it is not recommended where the roads are narrow, or the traffic heavy. For residential districts this class of kerb can be used with advantage. A combined form of concrete kerb and channel has been in use for a long time, but has never become popular owing to its weight and liability to damage in handling, and it can only be used in cases where the fall of the channel is parallel to that of the kerb. In all cases where a kerb, circular in plan, is required, the correct radius should be strictly observed, otherwise the effect is very displeasing.

CHANNELS

Channels formed of long flat stones are not provided on roads to the same extent as formerly. Mastic asphalt surfaces can be better finished off next to the kerb than outside a paved channel, which, by reason of its irregularity and number of joints, enables rainwater to percolate under the road surfacing, which may lead to its rapid destruction.

CHAPTER V

SUBSOIL AND DRAINAGE

UNTIL this subject of road construction assumed the status of an exact science, little heed had been paid to the importance of the subsoil, although McAdam, both by his teaching and practice, made it clear that the bearing capacity of the substratum was the most important feature in road construction. He argued, and correctly so, that the drier the bed, the higher was the resistance to pressure, and the greater the resilience or shock absorbing capacity. Consequently a longer life could be assumed for a road possessing these qualities.

Before deciding upon the kind of foundation to be provided for any road, it is necessary to open up a series of trial holes throughout the entire length of the route, as the subsoil may vary considerably. Road stability and permanence, success or failure, depend upon the quality of the subsoil on which the foundations are laid. If the substratum is of a soft, yielding, organic, or perishable nature, it will be useless to lay an ordinary type of foundation upon it. Each class of soil will require its own kind of treatment ; but, in every case, it is essential that it should be made hard and dry by draining and rolling.

CLAY SUBSOIL

The bearing capacity of subsoils may be assumed to range from one ton per foot super, a weight which a moist clay should be able to support. Owing to its capacity for retaining moisture, causing it to expand, and its subsequent contraction and cracking, owing to loss of water, during a spell of dry weather, clay must be regarded as the most dangerous of all subsoils. In addition to this, clay, when wet, is very liable to yield under traffic pressure, and to slide, chiefly in a lateral direction, and thereby to cause a complete collapse of the road structure. Some subsoils have a high rate of capillarity, and water will rise in them from a considerable depth. To ensure a dry substratum it is equally necessary to prevent the penetration or absorption of water from the surface of the road; but surface drainage must not be confounded with that of subsoil drainage. When dealing with a bad type of substratum, it is a difficult point to decide what should be done, in addition to drainage, to improve it. Curative methods have been attempted, such as the addition of 5% Portland cement, which decreases the volumetric changes due to moisture content, and increases the bearing capacity. Sand has been mixed with a clay subsoil, by ploughing or digging in, to provide porosity, and to reduce its hygroscopic properties; but it is doubtful if success can be relied upon in all cases, as clay so often occurs in a stratified formation overlaying earth and sand.

INSULATING COAT

If the subsoil has been adequately drained, the foundation work may be proceeded with, but in every case, except gravel or coarse sand, it is an excellent plan to provide a layer of ashes or clinker as an insulating or blanketing coat between the substratum and the bed of the foundation. This material should be spread over the shaped subsoil and only lightly rolled to a finished thickness of 3 to 6 inches, according to requirements. This layer, which has a high supporting value, will have the effect of decreasing the pressure on the substratum, as it enables concentrated traffic loads to be distributed over a larger area, and keeps the foundation dry by reducing capillary action.

LOAD DISTRIBUTION

Load distribution on the substratum has received some measure of attention, but it is a somewhat involved subject owing to the uncertain action of heavy high-speed vehicles. But sufficient is known about the subject to satisfy us that the intensity of pressure is greatest at the surface of the road, and that it diminishes radially through an angle of 45 degrees in a downward direction. The inter-relationship between substratum, foundation, and surface is, therefore, quite clear, and it is evident that the wearing coat must be more resistant than the foundation, or that its limit of elasticity should be greater.

The question may be raised as to whether the under-bed, the substratum on which the foundation rests, should be shaped to the correct surface camber of the road when finished. The answer to such a question would be no, but subject to modification. The careful shaping of the substratum may be a waste of money because, being of so soft a nature, it is impossible to maintain its shape as soon as work is commenced upon it. On the other hand, economy is ministered to by a judicious use of pegs, fixed to correct levels, so that more earth is not excavated than the case demands. The least amount of substratum disturbance, after the excavation has been made, and before the materials for the foundation have been applied, is an excellent rule to be observed on all road works.

Coarse gravel and sandy soils permit the easy passage of water, by reason of their porosity, but they part with it as rapidly by continuous percolation in all cases where the subsoil water is at a lower level. In consequence of this they form an ideal substratum for a road if there is no lateral flowing movement of the sand. In clay soils, and heavy loams, the particles of which they are formed are so very small that they retain a much greater volume of water. Clay will often retain twice as much water as a sandy loam. In peat, and any soil which contains organic matter, the water content is always high.

SATURATION

The saturation point of a sandy soil is 50% of volume, of light loam 56%, and clay 68%. The open spaces which exist between the particles comprising a soil, known as pore spaces, govern its water-holding capacity ; and in all soils the water content is higher nearer the surface owing to the presence of organic matter. In no soil is the water content so dangerous an element as it is with clay, because water modifies its load-bearing capacity. A wet clay may, in an unstable condition, be unable to support a quarter of a ton per foot super, but the same clay, when dry, could support twenty to twenty-five times that weight.

DRAINAGE

It is a remarkable fact that so important a matter as the draining of the road bed, on which the stability of the road crust depends, has only in recent years received the attention which its importance demands. No road, however well it may be constructed, can stand up against the needs of modern traffic unless the subsoil is kept dry and in an elastic condition, and this can only be secured by adequate drainage. Water, the most potent destroyer of all roads, attacks the base of the structure in three ways, viz. by saturation from the wet condition of the surrounding area ; by capillary attraction (the mechanical operation of which is facilitated by traffic vibration) ; and the penetration of water from the road surface. Drainage work, which should always be regarded as an integral part of the foundation, must be designed with care, so that all water may be allowed to pass off or rather to flow away to a lower level or point of discharge without hindrance. The elasticity or bearing capacity of the subsoil depends more upon its dryness than upon any other condition.

ROADSIDE DITCHES

It has been accepted up to this time that for most rural areas the digging out of a longitudinal ditch, on each side of a road, is a sufficient provision for drainage. It frequently happened that the roadside ditch was improperly graded, and instead of allowing water to flow away it remained stagnant, and water, in consequence, continued at a constant level under the road. The bed of a roadside ditch should be 18 inches wide, and the depth, which will vary with circumstances, should be such that the water level should never rise more than 12 inches below the level of the crown or centre of the road. An open ditch is also a source of weakness, as it considerably reduces the sectional area of the abutment or that strip which lies between the edge of the road and the ditch, sometimes called a water table. On the stability of this strip much depends. Since the introduction of heavy high-speed vehicles a considerable lateral thrust is exerted, which, in the absence of a kerb, causes a movement, and the creep of the surface materials of which the road is formed. Where a road is suffering deformation from such a cause, timber revetment should be used, or the ditch piped in and filled up with hard clean pressure-resisting material. The first sign of damage is noted by the sinking down of the road and loss of convexity in shape. It has been erroneously imagined by some that drainage is a costly matter, but a moment's thought will show that, as the bearing capacity of a subsoil when drained is so much enhanced, the cost of foundations may be reduced and economy obtained by a less thickness of foundation. Further, a road with a stable subsoil requires the minimum of maintenance, and is, in addition, a satisfactory road at all times, demanding the least attention to surface conditions.

DRAINAGE OF RURAL ROADS

The best method of draining the subsoil of a rural road, where much water is encountered, is to lay open-jointed land drain pipes transversely, with the longitudinal axis of the road, at a distance of 30 to 60 feet apart, as circumstances, varying with the amount of water, require. Trenches 12 to 18 inches deep and 9 to 15 inches wide are excavated in the subsoil and, in the bed, a semicircular groove is made in which the pipes are laid. This arrangement enables the line to be accurately kept and each pipe to be benched with clay to half its depth to prevent the escape of water into the subsoil. After the pipes have been laid, with falls towards the sides of the road, the trenches are filled in with clean gravel, clinker, or brick rubble. Equally important is the construction and grading of the gravitating drains on each side of the road which receive the discharge from the various transverse drains when laid as described. These roadside or longitudinal drains should be laid at a depth, if possible, of 12 inches below the lowest part of the transverse drains. The diameter of the pipes of the discharging drain will depend upon the number of cross drains and the gradient at which it can be laid to secure an uninterrupted outlet. The drain can be constructed of second quality salt glazed pipes, and junctions should be provided to pick up the transverse or cross drains. These roadside or receiving drains could, if properly designed, serve the dual purpose of dealing with the subsoil water, as described, and for passing off surface water.

On rural roads and where, in urban areas, a separate system of storm water and soil sewers exists, brick-built catchpits in lieu of trapped gully inlets, may be built, as they provide easy means for catching silt. These catchpits, like the ordinary street and roadside gullies, require constant attention, otherwise they defeat the very object for which they have been provided.

TREE ROOTS

In the vicinity of kerb-side trees, it is advisable to make the joints of the longitudinal drains with cement, otherwise roots will soon find their way into the pipes and render them useless, This insidiously slow growth can produce disastrous results, because it remains unsuspected until damage has been done to the road. If the trench, in which the side drain is laid, is not properly filled in and well consolidated, an elongated source of weakness will exist where the greatest possible capacity for resisting lateral pressure is required. In the disposal of surface water from the road the number of inlets, either street gullies, or catch-pits, will depend upon the gradient of the road, and the number of variations in gradient. Inlets for the water discharging drains must be provided at every change of grade, and also at intermediate places; and the distances apart will vary with every road.

In places where, owing to excessive gradients, storm water may have a destructive velocity, it will be necessary to pave the channels of country roads in the same way as is done for most roads in urban areas. The construction of drains, for the discharge of storm water, does not always receive the same care and attention as is bestowed upon soil sewers, that is to say, sewers for the discharge of sewage matter. This should not be the case, for the proper grading or laying to correct falls is as essential in the one case as the other, perhaps more essential in the case of storm water drains, owing to the heavy road detritus which is washed into them during periods of heavy rainfall.

SUBSOIL DRAINAGE OF TOWN STREETS

In the case of town streets, subsoil drainage cannot be provided in the way that has been described, as the conditions are very different. In residential districts, the level of the subsoil water is generally much lower than that of the road foundation. For such areas, the deep longi-tudinal sewers have to be depended upon without the shallow cross drains; but, in wet subsoils, the elongated sump-like action of such deep sewers can be increased by placing tiles around the pipes of which such sewers are built, or by the provision of invert blocks or land drain pipes under the sewers.

As alternatives to that described, the following methods may be found useful—

When road construction necessitates cutting, as on a hill slope, where the ground rises away from the road, it is advisable to lay a drain on the side of the high ground to intercept infiltration water, and prevent its passage into the foundation of the road. On the opposite side, as the ground slopes away, adequate natural provision exists to maintain the subsoil in a dry condition without recourse to any system of pipe drainage.

In the case of an existing road or one proposed to be laid out where the adjoining land is level with or higher than the road surface, double side drains for intercepting infiltration water may prove sufficient for all practical purposes without the transverse or cross drains laid in the herring-bone manner described.

Deeper subsoil drainage may, owing to peculiar geological conditions, and where springs occur, be found necessary, as, for instance, where an impervious clay underlies, at a depth of about 4 feet, an upper stratum of soil of a more porous texture. In such a case the land drain pipes should be laid on the clay to prevent its saturation under the road bed.

For roads near rivers or large sheets of water, where the subsoil level in the water courses and ditches is high, every effort should be made to stop percolation into the road foundation. This can be done by digging out trenches parallel with the roadway below the water level, and filling them with well-puddled clay. A substantial layer, 6 to 12 inches deep, of clean hard clinker should be laid on the subsoil to prevent the rise of water, by capillary attraction, into the road foundation. No other means of drainage or preventive measures would suffice. These trenches ought to be excavated as far from the roadway as possible, and should be properly constructed of a width not less than 2 feet and of the full depth required. This method has proved very satisfactory. In similar instances, fascines have been found useful for carrying a roadway over a water-logged area when all other means have failed.

CHAPTER VI

FOUNDATIONS

THROUGHOUT the ages, and until very recent years, roads have been so made as to consist entirely of foundations or —without them. Paradoxical as this may appear to be, it nevertheless represents the line of action of those who have been entrusted with the task of making and maintaining the highways of the kingdom. The idea which occupied the minds of the ancients seems to have been bent in the direction of massiveness, and large blocks of stone bedded on the earth served as a foundation and a wearing surface. Later, though still in the period defined as B.C., we have records that roads were actually constructed with smaller materials held together by a matrix of sand and earth ; but here again both foundation and surface coat were one and the same. Ancient causeways, formed with large irregularly shaped blocks of stone, which archaeologists insist are of pre-Roman date, are to be found in this country, and we are familiar with the same method of construction in the ancient cities of the world. During the period known as the Dark Ages, but which might be more properly styled the middle era, from the fifth to the fifteenth century, it is evident that the art of road making was lost, but when it began to be recovered, first of all in the large centres of population, paving with stones was reintroduced.

RIVAL THEORIES

When John Loudon McAdam began his operations, at the end of the eighteenth century, it is evident, from the piecing together of contemporary references, that however bad the roads were at that time, some effort had been previously made to provide them with foundations. McAdam argued, from first to last, that foundations were not essential, and in all his undertakings he proceeded to "lift" (his own term) the larger stones in the bed, which he caused to be broken into smaller pieces and replaced on the road surface. Broken stone, used as the wearing surface of a road, and laid in the manner specified by this indefatigable road maker, has, since his day, been known as macadam. Telford, a contemporary of McAdam, on the other hand, argued that a foundation was necessary ; and for every road constructed by him he required, between the subsoil and the wearing surface, hand-pitched stones 7 inches in depth, tops 3 inches in width, and the interstices, or spaces between these large stones, filled with smaller ones. Modern practice demands adequate foundations, and these are provided in three ways, viz. the Telford system, the pell-mell distribution of "hardcore," and concrete laid as a monolithic slab.

FOUNDATION CALCULATIONS NECESSARY

In the design of foundations either for a new road, or for the improvement of an existing one, it is no longer possible to depend upon rule of thumb methods. The information required to enable the necessary calculations to be made is the character of the subsoil (revealed by sinking trial holes), and the weight, character and intensity of the traffic to be carried. Let it be assumed that the subsoil consists of clay, or some other unstable earth, and that it would be unwise to estimate its bearing capacity when untreated for a dead or static load at more than one and a half tons to the foot super, and that the vehicles to be carried over the proposed road are of a heavy fast-moving self-propelled type. The axle load of a heavy motor, will often exceed in practice, eight tons, and whether legally allowed or not, it is advisable to make the calculations on the basis of an axle load of more than 5 tons, on each rear wheel. But it is not the static weight which interests the road maker, it is the live load he has to cater for, and it is for this most destructive agency that provision has to be made.

ROAD IMPACT SHOCKS

It is recognized in practice, and from theoretical tests that have been made, that impact shock depends to a very considerable extent upon the kind and condition of tyres. Solid rubber tyres in course of time became almost as hard and unyielding as steel, and when worn thin could deliver impact blows of equal severity.

From the minutes of the proceedings of the Institution of Civil Engineers, which recorded the results of experiments on the impact of wheels on roads, it is noted that—

" (1) Overloading the tyre contributes more to excessive vibration than does any other factor.

" (2) Provided that the tyre is not overloaded, the amplitudes of vertical and horizontal vibration attain a maximum when the radius of a hollow in the road is equal to that of the tyre.

" (3) A definite characteristic of an overloaded tyre is a rapid increase in the amplitude of horizontal vibration when the speed exceeds a critical value.

" (4) Above a vehicle-speed of 10 m.p.h., the vibrations recorded are influenced by surface irregularities preceding the obstruction, since these cause movements of the chassis which persist during the passage over the obstacle.

" (5) When the radius of a hollow in the road surface exceeds that of the tyre, the amplitude of vibration is considerably influenced by the magnitude of the unsprung weight.

" (6) When the vehicle passes over a raised obstruction, the amplitude of vibration is influenced much more by tyre resilience and total unsprung weight than by wheel size.

" (7) Observations of spring-deflection give little or no useful indication of the wheel-load, owing to the outweighing influence of the axle inertia forces." And, further, that: "The energy dissipated during impact is greater for a solid tyre than for a pneumatic tyre, and this results in a greater decrement in the height of rebound and a consequent reduction in the number of rebounds before the amplitude becomes negligibly small. The energy dissipated appears to increase less rapidly than the total energy absorbed, and thus the decrement increases as the amplitude of rebound decreases. Regular cavities and hollows in an otherwise solid tyre, by reducing its stiffness, give it properties intermediate between a plain solid tyre and pneumatic tyre, but resembling the former more than the latter."

It has been ascertained by careful tests that impact may be as high as seven times the static load on one rear wheel, fitted with a solid tyre, when such wheel strikes a one-inch obstruction at a speed of 16 miles per hour. But for all practical purposes, as modern roads can be provided with smooth wearing surfaces, the force of impact may be taken as 10 tons or twice the static load on one of the rear wheels. If the questions of drainage and of subsoil stability have been properly considered to secure permanent dry condition, then it ought to be possible to improve the subsoil to such an extent that its bearing capacity will be equal to 2 tons per square foot.

HARDCORE FOUNDATIONS

Whatever type of base may be adopted—" Telford," hardcore, or concrete—it is advisable to interpose between the subsoil and the foundation bed a layer or " blanket " course of clinker ashes. This material should be hard, well burnt, free from dust, and should be lightly rolled to a thickness of 3 to 6 inches. It furnishes a layer of insulating materials which prevents the capillary creep of water. In laying down hardcore foundations two systems of construction, as already mentioned, can be pursued—the method known as the " Telford " or the placing of each piece of material in a progressive manner across the width of the carriageway; or the unloading from motor-driven lorries and the spreading of the materials in a pell-mell manner over the area. Whichever method is adopted, it is essential that the materials shall be sound, hard, durable, and free from dust. No stone, piece of old

concrete, brickwork, or vitrified brick should exceed
9 inches in size—5 to 9 inches is permissible. When this
material is laid by hand it should be bedded on its broadest
face, the narrow part uppermost, and each course should
be made to break joint, as far as is possible with this
class of material—continuous joints must be avoided. On
completion, the projecting pieces should be knapped off
and the interstices carefully filled with broken stone, of a
size from $2\frac{1}{2}$ to 1 inch, and the whole very carefully dry
rolled. The weight of the roller is important, and one of
eight tons is more likely to secure better results than a
heavier one, for reasons to be considered later. This
foundation coat, after the materials of which it is composed
(the larger stones and the smaller ones for filling the interstices) have been dry rolled, should be blinded or smoothed
off with a cementitious slurry, in which the maximum
quantity of $\frac{3}{4}$ inch stone chippings are used. In the preparation of the slurry, the excessive use of water should be avoided
as the wetting of the subsoil weakens its bearing capacity.

The second system of construction is the pell-mell
method of spreading the materials. When this has been
done, the rolling and finishing off can be carried out in the
same manner as that which has been described for hand-
pitching ; but a ten-ton roller can be more safely used for
this class of work.

JOINTS AND VOIDS IN FOUNDATION

On completion, by either method, a very substantial mass
should result, which should be capable of resisting the
vibratory stresses, set up by the rolling action of wheels, as
well as the impact shocks of heavily loaded vehicles. Both
systems will reveal a high percentage of voids in the mass.
The objection to hand-pitching arises from the very
perfection of its manner of construction, as it contains the
maximum number of vertical joints, up which it is possible
for the subsoil to be forced by the displacement of earth
due to the pressing down action of the roller, for which

reason an eight-ton roller is better than one of ten tons weight.

In the other method—the pell-mell system—the joints are both vertical and horizontal; this, though minimizing the risk of the upward movement of earth throughout the mass, produces a large number of voids, and, as a result, greater interstitial movement and wear. The presence of finely divided earthy matter between the pieces forming the foundation of a road is an element of weakness as, in the event of a damp subsoil and insufficient insulation by means of clinker ashes, as already described, water may penetrate by capillary attraction the whole crust—foundation and wearing coat. Further, when the surface of the road has become worn, or has lost its water-proofness, rainwater may pass to the subsoil through the many vertical joints. In either case a wet condition of subsoil and surface of road has to be guarded against to prevent the breakdown of the structure.

OPENING ROAD BEFORE COMPLETION

After the foundation has been prepared in the manner described, the road should be opened and traffic of all descriptions allowed to travel over it for as long a period as possible before the surface or wearing coat is applied. The camber should be somewhat greater than the finished surface, to enable storm water to pass off to the sides of the road as quickly as possible. The continuous rolling effect of vehicular traffic will be much more advantageous than systematic steam rolling, as the irregularities of the unfinished surface will cause impact blows to be delivered, which, on transmission through the mass to the subsoil, will expose the weak places. These can be treated by strengthening or taking out, and by complete reconstruction, where required, before the surface coat is laid. Each method of construction—hand-pitching or pell-mell—is very satisfactory, as the initial cost is generally low compared with any kind of concrete foundation ; and in addition, it provides a more resilient base, an item of considerable importance in determining the life of a road. Another great advantage over concrete is in the time factor. With concrete, unless the more expensive quick-setting cements are used, or where, if there is sufficient width, half the road can be made at a time, the road must be closed for a considerable period. With hardcore, half the road can be dealt with at a time, and the transit of vehicles, provided the traffic may be classed as "Medium" and not "Heavy," encouraged for the purpose of assisting the work of consolidation.

OLD ROAD OR NEW FOUNDATION

Whenever it is possible to utilize an old water bound macadam road, which has not been disturbed by frequent opening for domestic services, it should be used in preference to a new foundation, for the very reasons which have been adduced for passing traffic over a new hardcore foundation. Levels do not often permit of this, but it is a point to be borne in mind. An extra thickness of wearing coat will often more than compensate for the theoretical loss due to the absence of new foundations.

In the work of reconstruction, where funds do not permit of complete new foundations, any road, particularly a road of a rural character, can be strengthened by the provision of new abutments of hard suitable materials in the haunches, continuous mass concrete for preference. This should occupy a total width of one-third of the roadway—one-sixth on each side. If hardcore materials are used, this should be extended to half the total width of the carriage-way, or one-quarter on each side of the road.

If adequate subsoil drainage does not exist, it is an essential matter to provide for the maintenance of a dry subsoil by means of elongated trenches on both sides of the road, 2 feet wide and 18 inches deep. These trenches should be filled with coarse hard burnt clinker, closely packed. Lateral support is necessary for both foundation

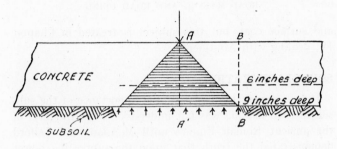

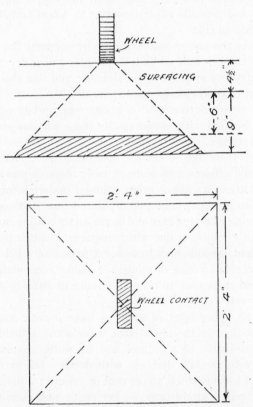

DIAGRAM SHOWING HOW PRESSURE ON FOUNDATIONS
IS DISTRIBUTED

(From a paper by Mr. O. Cattlin, Borough Engineer of Lambeth,
delivered before the Institution of Municipal and County Engineers
in London, on the 15th Jan., 1926.)

and surface coat, but this subject is treated in Chapter IV, dealing with Abutments.

SOIL STABILIZATION

It is a remarkable fact that the importance of the sub-soil in road making was not understood from the days of the ancient Roman Empire until McAdam and Telford demonstrated the truth that upon the supporting power of the soil depends road stability. McAdam laid it down as an axiom that—

"It is the native soil which really supports the weight of the traffic; that while it is preserved in a dry state it will carry any weight without sinking; and that this native soil must be previously made quite dry."

The term "native soil" is a very appropriate one, and might be used with advantage by those who are studying this problem.

Some years ago, when the benefits to be derived from stabilized subsoils were realized, early research proved that the addition of sand or other granular materials improved an unsuitable soil, and that hydrated lime decreased the volumetric change of clay and increased its bearing capacity. That this subject is one which requires scientific handling is evident, as soils may have a dry appearance yet hold a considerable amount of moisture—sandy loam with 8 per cent and chalk with 10 per cent volume of water would not be suspect.

In the upper layer of soils, as more organic matter is present than in the lower ones, more water is held; but the pore-spaces of a subsoil and its water content, due directly to rainfall, decrease with depth. The saturation point of a sandy soil is 50 per cent of volume; a light loam, 50 per cent; sandy peat, 63 per cent; and clay, 68 per cent. Dryness is only a comparative term, and is not desirable, as a certain amount of moisture in a soil is necessary to maintain its stability.

In U.S.A., soil stabilization has been defined as a process

which aims at "properly combining natural soils so that the granular material is surrounded with just enough binder to produce a dense weather-resisting layer. To possess maximum density and stability, the mixture must have a minimum of voids after compaction, which means that it must be held together by a cohesive agent such as clay." This definition points to the fact that work in the United States has been in the direction of producing a stabilized soil mortar, and that moisture, which only holds the particles together by reason of its surface tension forces, an unstable and uncertain element due to climatic variations, has to be relied upon for cohesion.

Experience in this country, to which reference will be made, is demonstrating that soil stabilization need not be limited to American practice, but may, in fact, be quite different.

The scientific principles involved in the construction of the water-bound road were unknown in the days when broken stone or flints, earth, water, and brawn were regarded as the only essentials necessary for road making; yet the basic fact was understood, and upon it important knowledge has been founded. When sand, gravel or broken stone is added to a clay soil, or clay added to a granular soil, and just sufficient moisture is maintained by the addition of salts, the supporting power of the subsoil is increased.

Clay and moisture together act as the cohesive or binding agents, and the properties of the surface tension of moisture in holding particles together is illustrated in the case of a water-bound road, to which attention has already been drawn, and wet beach-sand, over which it is possible to drive heavy vehicles at high speeds. This property of cohesion or surface tension of moisture is due to the fact that the cohesive force between the molecules of a liquid is equal in all directions; consequently, for the maintenance of this force, the hygroscopic properties of salt will be appreciated.

In the U.S.A., where considerable progress has been made in the technique of soil treatment, and the use of stabilizers such as Portland cement, several types of bituminous materials, calcium chloride, and common salt (sodium chloride), it is argued that not only does the permanence of every kind of road depend on the stability of the subgrade, but also that the improvement of subgrade conditions warrants a less costly form of construction, a thinner bituminous wearing surface, and consequently a more resilient type of roadway. The saving in cost of construction and upkeep meets, it is contended, the cost of soil stabilization.

The following is the composition for a stabilized gravel road, based on U.S.A. practice: Graded coarse aggregate 55 per cent, graded fine aggregate 33 per cent, silt or clay binder, 12 per cent. To these, one of the stabilizers already mentioned may be added in quantities which practice alone can decide, but calcium chloride or sodium chloride is mixed with or applied to the compacted aggregates at the rate of ½ lb. per square yard per inch of depth to preserve the cohesive strength derived from the capillary moisture in the soil-binder. Dependent on climatic conditions, from one to three maintenance treatments of calcium chloride, ½ lb. per square yard, may be required during every season, if the stabilized base is unsurfaced, when the rainfall is at the minimum.

If the subsoil is not plastic enough to use as a binder, a dried and pulverized clay binder may be obtained locally or from a clay-pit in the district; and the granular material need not reach gravel size. The granular material commonly used is pit run and crushed gravel (maximum size, 1⅛ inches), or crusher-run limestone.

Where the traffic is fairly heavy, as in New York State, the gravel stabilized layer is built 9 inches thick at the centre line, 6 inches thick, 5 feet from the centre, and comes to a feather edge 10 feet from the centre, giving a width of 20 feet requiring slightly over 7,000 cubic yards of gravel per mile. Both calcium chloride and sodium chloride are used on these roads. The calcium salt is usually spread over the surface immediately after construction at the rate of 1·5 lb. per square yard; while the sodium salt is incorporated into the top 3 inches before finishing and used at the rate of 2 lb. per square yard.

On some roads the binding material is derived from the subgrade or ditches, in others from the gravel overburden or clayey layers interstratified with the gravel, but sometimes it is found necessary to open a special pit for the binder. Elsewhere than in the crusher-run limestone sections, uncrushed pit-run gravel is used, and on some sections pebbles up to $1\frac{1}{2}$ inches in size are not uncommon in a stabilized surface.

Practice in U.S.A. has demonstrated the usefulness of an asphalt or other type of bituminous surface-coat for these stabilized bases. Such a covering takes care of the wear and tear of traffic, and prevents the moisture content of the base from varying over too wide limits due to rain or rapid evaporation. In all such cases a less plastic mix lends itself more readily to a surfacing coat. Wherever such a surfacing has been applied, the roads have remained in excellent condition, and greater importance is attached to this kind of improvement than to mere base stabilized surfaces, as it gives all the advantages at much less cost.

As already indicated, this subject of soil stabilization is receiving attention in this country, but along lines different from those in the U.S.A. A theory has been propounded that any process in which even the smallest quantity of binder is employed cannot be depended on, as the incidence of water must always be a real hazard.

In the new approach to this subject, whilst the load-bearing capacity of the foundation is aimed at, the stabilizer does not act as a cement, a finding in contradistinction to American practice.

The overstressing of the subsoil—one of the most

destructive agencies in road stability—which soil stabilization seeks to reduce, is referred to later in this chapter.

THE OIL PROCESS OF STABILIZATION

I am indebted to Mr. H. Gardner, B.Sc., who submitted
a paper on this subject to the Institute of Petroleum.

The load-bearing capacity of a finely-graded system, for
instance, naturally-occurring soil, varies with the water
content, for which there is an optimum. The latter varies
with different soils, as also does the range of water contents,
termed the Useful Water Content Range, over which the
soil has a bearing capacity adequate for its intended purpose.

Bearing capacity varies, too, with the grading and, to
a certain extent, with the nature of the clay fraction.
Grading is under control; the appropriate material, fine
or coarse, may be added, and the swelling of clay may
be reduced by the addition of small quantities of
hydrated lime.

Hence, if a soil of suitable grading and nature be consolidated at a water content within the Useful Water Content Range, and if the water content be kept within that
range, the soil is stabilized.

Now, the binding properties of the water are derived
from the films of water between contiguous soil particles,
and it is important that those films be not displaced.
Herein lies the difference between the oil process and
others in which the stabilizer is a cementitious binder
wetting the soil particle by displacing, wholly or in part,
the water film. The oil which has been developed for this
process is one which spreads easily on water films and,
when spread, becomes rigid. By spreading over the water
films, it successfully reduces the rate of evaporation to
small magnitude; while, being both hydrophobic and, in
thin film, rigid, prevents the rise of water by capillarity
and its own consequent displacement.

Naturally, such treated soils have poor attrition resistance, and it is still necessary to apply a wearing carpet

which should be of an "impervious" type. Open-textured carpets may not be used. Rain penetrating such carpets is prevented from entering the stabilized foundation by the acquired hydrophobic property of the latter, and becomes trapped between carpet and foundation. Under the action of traffic the water becomes pounded into the foundation progressively, with bad effect on the bearing capacity of the latter.

The desirable characteristics of the stabilizer may be summarized as follows—

1. It should be highly hydrophobic.
2. It should spread easily on a water surface.
3. When spread in thin film it should acquire rigidity.
4. It should be capable of being mixed with the soil in conventional mixing plant in a reasonable time.
5. It should be stable.

This process has been applied to a wide range of soils in England, with results that indicate that the process is sound in principle. Even on a site where the winter water-table is at ground level, the water content of stabilized soil has remained substantially as when laid. Soil stabilization is a process which, when approached on sound well-founded lines, has a promising future.

OVERSTRESSING SUBSOIL

In the case of hardcore, the load distribution will not be the same as in a concrete foundation; consequently, unless a considerable factor of safety is allowed, there will be a serious danger of over-stressing the subsoil. But allowance to provide for this cannot be economically secured by increasing the thickness either of the foundation or of the wearing coat; consequently it is essential that everything should be done to make the subsoil capable of bearing as high a load as possible. A 3 to 6 inch consolidated layer of clinker ashes, which should always be interposed between the subsoil and the foundation, should have the effect of increasing the stability of the subsoil and making it equal to a bearing capacity of 2 tons per square foot at least.

Pressure, due to load, can be regarded as being radially distributed at an angle of 45° from the point of wheel contact at the road surface. In a well consolidated macadam road crust, from 9 to 12 inches thick, this pressure would be spread over an area of 5 square feet. As the impact shock may be equal to 10 tons, it will be seen that a heavy loaded vehicle travelling from 15 to 20 miles per hour, can do serious damage to such a road if the surface is in any way deformed or rough. The extent of permanent injury depends to a considerable extent upon the resilient qualities of the wearing coat, the foundation, and the subsoil. Where a measure of resilience has been provided by the methods of construction outlined in this chapter, sufficient to overcome the temporary deformation, that is to say, within the limits of elasticity, damage may not result from an impact shock of even greater intensity.

SALVAGE OF OLD ROAD FOUNDATIONS

In the construction of roads, the ratepaying public is brought into close contact with this class of public works, and criticisms of modern road construction methods have appeared from time to time in the Press. One of these has reference to the removal of old concrete foundations and their replacement by new materials. The cause of these complaints sometimes arose from the fact that the putting in of a new foundation meant the closing of the road for a longer period than for resurfacing only, leading to the disorganization of traffic. But often the complaints were due to the ignorant idea that such new foundation was altogether unnecessary. The critics overlooked the fact that the intensity, weight, and speed of traffic have enormously increased since many of the old concrete foundations were laid, and that most of them were, in places, depressed by the weight of traffic, cracked, laminated by shear stresses or disintegrated. All these old concrete foundations have suffered from the hammer-like blows of heavy high-speed vehicles, due, often, to the inequalities of the running surface of the road.

One of the favourite suggestions put forward by the uninformed critics has been that the whole of the old concrete foundation could be saved if another layer of concrete were placed on the top of it, but this overlooked two important points. First of all, it is just possible in most cases that the level would not permit; and, in the second place, a weakness, due to lamination, would occur if the concrete (the whole mass) were not homogeneous, the strength of concrete being due to its monolithic character.

If an old concrete foundation presents, when exposed for expert inspection, only superficial damage, a few slight cracks, and no laminations, then it might be debated whether it should be utilized for a new running surface or not. If it is decided to salvage the old concrete, this can be successfully accomplished by means of two-coat rolled asphalt. The base course, varying in thickness from $1\frac{1}{2}$ inches, to obtain the original levels, would take up all the surface inequalities of the concrete; and the surface coat, of from 1 inch to $1\frac{1}{2}$ inch, would afford a level and un-yielding surface, with properties to minimize traffic shocks. The base course would thus act as a cushion for the absorption of impact blows. It is in some such circum-stances as these that it might be possible to save the old concrete foundation of a road, reduce the cost of recon-struction, and minimize any further destructive effects upon it of heavy high-speed traffic.

CHAPTER VII

MOTORWAYS AND MISCELLANEOUS MATTERS

OF the many post-war problems with which we are confronted in these days, the two most pressing relate to town-planning and transport, but the two are inseparable and make together one economic problem of unparalleled magnitude. The problem must be solved by a sagacious development of the existing highways; control of traffic by signals, and the provision of new routes for the better segregation of traffic. Much criticism is being levelled at the Government's road policy because at present it is only proposed to experiment with new motorways in sections as soon as it is possible to do so. The great danger of sectional road development is the production of bottlenecks, of which far too many exist already. But is the criticism altogether justified? No, it is not, and for these reasons: We cannot possibly expect to maintain our supremacy as a highly industrialized nation in the production of heavy goods, plant, and machinery as in the past, as, owing to the war, these goods are now produced in greater quantities than ever before in the U.S.A., throughout the Empire, and even India. We can, however, expect much development in the production of the lighter types of precision goods; and our agricultural industry must continue to develop until we can grow sufficient food for minimum national needs. Further, it is not yet known to what extent the population of congested areas will be dispersed to meet these new conditions, neither is it yet certain how the numbers may be reduced by war, or augmented by the influx of foreigners, or how the balance may be upset by the decline in the birth-rate and other contingencies.

Another plea made against the extreme modernizing

of the highways comes from the great number of private-car owners, who, in the past, motored mainly for pleasure, and who could not endure the boredom of commercialized roads and who would give up motoring. On the other hand, it is admitted that more and more commercial roads are badly needed as traffic arteries for goods, passengers, and commercial travellers.

No solution of the problem will be possible until from the minds of everybody has been removed the fallacy that as road traffic is detrimental to railway interests, it must be kept in check. In this highly industrialized and congested land there is ample scope for both systems of transport, and they must work together without antagonism. The nation cannot afford to allow the railways to be ruined nor road transport undeveloped to bolster up the railways. It has to be remembered that every citizen is a shareholder in the national highway system, worth probably £2,000,000,000, though his dividends are not paid to him in cash.

Up to this time the road transport system has followed the precedent of railway organization. Owing to the rapid growth of the railway services in the early days, it became necessary to differentiate between the method of working the expresses and the slow trains, which last-named service became known as "local," a designation which denoted its limited and circumscribed area of operations. To-day, however, both services are worked over the same "roads," owing to the perfected railway systems. It is this fact which compels the inquiry—are motorways necessary, and cannot the highways of this country (those already in existence and those now being planned) be adapted to carry all kinds of traffic—through, local, heavy, light, speedy, and slow?

The problem awaits an answer; but, in the meantime, if a motorway is defined, it may enable all students of the subject to form an opinion.

A motorway is a highway or route which is designed for

mechanically-propelled high-speed vehicles, and approximates as nearly as possible to a railway, except that its terminal points are not at, and its alignment does not run through, important or congested centres of population. It is isolated by means of wide grass verges, suitably planted with trees and shrubs, and devoid of advertising hoardings and other blots on the landscape, without any vestige of ribbon development; but, unlike the railways, has no level-crossings. Branch roads cross it by means of over-bridges or subways; and essential junctions join it in the same direction as the main traffic stream.

Each motorway should, if possible, be an entity with two or more tracks as required, that is to say, the one for up traffic should be separated completely from the one for down traffic, the distance between each varying with physical, historical, and economic conditions. This complete segregation of the two types of traffic, up and down, prevents the danger of glare from the head-lights of on-coming vehicles; obviates the central strip of useless and expensive-to-maintain waste for dividing the traffic; and facilitates alignment, making it easier to bring wider areas in the same locality into closer contact with each by means of connecting or feeder roads.

To prevent the boredom which is inseparable from miles of undeviating routes and to secure variety of scenery, long, straight stretches should be avoided; and all curves, including transition curves, should have a clear vision of never less than a quarter of a mile, and should be super-elevated with mathematical precision to prevent the possibility of vehicles overturning when travelling at high speeds.

To reduce tractive effort, steep gradients should be avoided, as, in the approximation to the railways, the new types of road vehicles to be evolved may follow the train system of trailers; an approximate equivalent of rail smoothness may be obtained with a skid-proof running surface, one which offers the least resistance to rolling, has fewest irregularities to minimize impact shocks, and provides the additional resilience, to that of the vehicle, to overcome axle friction and other retarding and destructive forces.

The motorway should be the most practical solution of the economics of highway long-distance transport, which, when sensibly linked with and not in opposition to rail transport, should be expected to solve, not by revolution, but by progressive and peaceful evolution, some of the most pressing problems of transport which confront us in these times.

STREETS IN BUILT-UP AREAS

The layout of streets in the past was allowed to proceed in so haphazard a manner that the coming of the unexpected motor transport vehicles created unsatisfactory conditions on highways, roads, and streets of populated areas which are difficult to remedy. The chance to improve upon old conditions has, in many places, been made possible by bomb destruction of property. The solution, however, is not an easy one, as there are more than two schools of thought on the subject of the design and layout of roads and streets in built-up areas.

To reduce the amount of traffic in any centre of population to that which is of local importance only, it will be necessary to divert all through traffic on to radial roads, ring roads, and by-passes. In addition to this, other roads of a ring-like character should be constructed to facilitate the local traffic; and streets, particularly residential ones, should, where possible, be closed to all types of through traffic.

In the development of these improvements, the following points must also be borne in mind—

1. The installation of traffic signals for the control of vehicles and pedestrians.

2. The provision of parking places for the cars of local residents when shopping or visiting; and the provision

of further parking places for people coming into the town.

3. The fixing of suitable positions for pedestrian crossing places; guard rails; roundabouts and refuges; subways or overbridges.

4. In all newly built-up areas, subways should be provided for sewers, water and gas pipes, and for all cables.

5. Service roads at the rear of premises in busy shopping districts are necessary for the delivery of goods, as a single stationary vehicle reduces the traffic capacity of a street.

6. Areas for shops to be clearly defined in all places where reconstruction permits or is necessary; or where a new area is laid out.

7. Footpaths to be of sufficient width, having regard to local conditions, and surfaced so as not to be inferior to the surface of the carriage-way.

8. The kind of kerb to be used, whether to be round, square, or splayed front edge; height above channel, and maximum radius at street junctions.

9. The materials to be employed in surfacing the carriage-ways and footpaths. This has become an important subject, as in future it is probable that such surfaces will be washed down by means of hose pipes (using water under pressure from the mains), and street scavenging, as at present, discontinued.

10. Of the amenities to be considered, the following should not be overlooked—

(a) The provision of distinctly lettered street-name plates in correct positions.

(b) Whether trees should be planted or not.

(c) Should any particular street be regarded as for one-way traffic only—a decision which will require much consideration, as such a type of street is always a danger to pedestrians.

Attention is drawn to the Ministry of War Transport's Memorandum No. 575, and their Report (1946) on "Design and Layout of Roads in Built-up Areas."

ROAD AND STREET LIGHTING

The question of more and better road and street lighting is now receiving the serious attention of the Local
Authorities, and a Departmental Committee of the Government recently issued an Interim Report. It is computed
that in England the night traffic is 85 per cent of the
day traffic, whilst in France, Belgium and Switzerland
it is 75, 75 and 70 per cent respectively. And yet the
lighting of busily trafficked roads is still in an immature
and chaotic state, thereby causing not only a number of
preventable and fatal accidents but also discounting the
economic value of our wonderful road system. Imagine the
position of our railways if they could not be used at night
time owing to the absence of light signals. Their economic
plight would be worse than it is at present and traffic
chaos would result. In America this subject of road illumination, outside the built-up areas, has received much more
attention than in this country, and it has been proved
that night accidents on the roads could be considerably reduced by better and more scientifically planned illumination.

The Highway Research Board of America has made a
series of investigations into this subject, and the result of
their findings coincides with that of the National Safety
Council. In New Jersey, America, 44 per cent of the total
accidents and 55 per cent of the fatalities occurred at night;
whilst in this country 58 per cent of all fatal motor vehicle
accidents occurred after nightfall. In other words, more
than half the accidents occur when the volume of traffic
is at its lowest. It will thus be noted that the efficient
lighting of the highways and streets is one of the most
pressing of the many road problems which await solution.

In Germany this question of street and highway lighting
has received attention and many tests have been made.
From a pre-war German source, as recorded in the "Road
Abstracts," issued by the Ministry of Transport, it is learned
that tests to date have demonstrated that—"The elimination of shadow involves the removal of trees close to the

WESTERN AVENUE, MIDDLESEX: CYCLIST TRACK
(Photo: *Tecart Studios, London, W.C.1*)

road margin; the growth of other trees must be restricted if it is likely to interfere with the distribution or reflection of artificial light. Centrally suspended lights in series of 500-watt lamps are preferred, but equally satisfactory results have been obtained with 600 to 700-watt lamps placed beside the carriageway. It is pointed out that too high a standard of illumination is likely to result in fatigue and decreased sensitiveness of vision, and that glare may be prevented by the use of frosted globes. The height at which lamps are placed is of great importance, as if the lamps are placed too low, the distribution of light is uneven, vehicle lights, and especially signal lights, become less easily distinguishable, and the shapes and sizes of objects in the carriageway are less accurately estimated. On roads where traffic is heavy, a height of 26 to 30 ft. above the carriageway is recommended; in the case of roads of minor importance the height should be 21 to 23 ft."[1]

TREES

In one of the issues of "Road Abstracts" published by the Ministry of Transport, it is noted that:—"Apart from their value in increasing the beauty of roads and streets, and in affording shade, trees planted along the roadside are easily recognized at night, or in fog or snow. Their visibility may if necessary be improved by painting the trunks white. Trees afford the most natural and suitable means of roadside marking in open country; in wooded areas, however, suitably painted posts should be provided. In tree planting consideration must be given to the maintenance of a clear view for traffic, to the position and width of the road, and to the type of soil and climate. New planting on one side of the road only should allow an interval of 50 to 60 ft. from tree to tree; a staggered formation should be adopted when planting on both sides of the road. The interval in this case should be 80 to 100 ft. Where footways

[1] Recently modified to 25 feet and 15 feet respectively.

are provided, trees should be planted on the side away from the kerb about 20 in. from the outer margin."

CYCLE TRACKS

In consequence of the large number of cyclists and the many accidents which befall them on the highways, it is remarkable that the opposition of their organized bodies should be so vehement against the provision of special tracks for the use of cyclists. On the Continent, and particularly in Holland, the necessity has been recognized and special tracks, parallel with the highways, have been extensively constructed. In Italy and Germany the matter was under consideration and steps were being taken to segregate this kind of traffic. When the track follows the alignment of the road it is necessary to provide sufficient access to and from it. There is no necessity to provide a track on each side of the road—the argument in favour of double-tracked carriageways cannot be advanced for cyclists—but for a single track 30 inches wide should be sufficient or from 5 to 6 feet for a two-way track, though it should be made wider if possible. The foundations for cycle tracks need only be light, and the surface may be constructed of materials similar to those employed in made-up footways. In all cases it is necessary to provide a planted strip, or a fence, between the carriage-way or footway to ensure the safety of both cyclists and pedestrians.

The Minister of Transport in his speech which was broadcast on the 2nd January, 1936, on what he called "the vital balance sheet for 1935," stated, *inter alia*, that: "Another fact which I fear may emerge from the final analysis of the whole country is the problem presented by the growth of pedal cycling. I have London figures before me and they show an alarming increase in the number of casualties in which pedal cyclists are involved at a time when we have not only checked but actually reduced the number of accidents in which pedestrians and other road users are concerned. I feel that we could considerably narrow the scope of our problem if during the year we would pay more regard to pedal cyclists, and if pedal cyclists would pay more regard to themselves. I might perhaps remind them of the provisions in the Highway Code, intended to preserve the common interest, which call upon them to proceed not more than two abreast, and where conditions warrant, in single file, and also not to cut out or cut in. If I ask them, and indeed everyone else, to follow the provisions of the Highway Code, it is in the honest conviction that some lives which would undoubtedly otherwise be lost will be saved."

GRASS VERGES

The Ministry of War Transport's Memorandum No. 575 recommended, wherever possible, the provision of verges of ample width between paved areas, to separate cycle tracks from carriageways, and for the planting of trees.

The recommendations should prove very acceptable, as footpaths have become so essential for safety. In the past they have been neglected, and pedestrians have maintained their legal right to walk on the carriage-way, which, in places, is better for that purpose than the footpath.

A verge or greensward, not less than 3 feet wide, with trees, makes a more pleasing footway than one that is wholly impervious. When grass margins are properly maintained they add a quiet charm to a district and are one of the few amenities of our residential road system that a speed-ridden generation enjoys.

CHAPTER VIII

SURFACING AND FOOTWAYS

THE average man on the road, who is first cousin to the well-known " man in the street," is only interested in the surface of the road over which he travels. He does not consider the many factors which are employed in the scientific construction of the road ; nor the problems which are inseparable from its maintenance.

SURFACING

In the design and construction of a highway, the road maker has to keep the following points in view, and be certain that his perspective in each case is a correct one.

1. Rapidity of construction, essential owing to traffic demands, and, in business quarters, to the loss which tradesmen suffer when roads are closed.

2. The surface must be impervious to moisture, as water either in or under a road, is a most destructive element.

3. It should remain unaffected by climatic conditions, and be able to withstand extremes of temperature without injury, or permanent deformation.

4. Dust and mud can never again be tolerated, as there is no longer any reason for these evidences of uneconomical methods of construction.

5. Slipperiness, which is inherent in all types of homogeneous surfacing materials, should be guarded against to minimize its extent.

6. Durability is essential, and the test of a good road lies in the cost per yard super, arrived at by dividing first cost by the number of years of its life.

7. It must be capable of dealing with all types of vehicles and all speeds of traffic.

8. It is necessary that it should be so constructed that trench openings and repairs can be expeditiously carried out.

9. It should be as even and noiseless as possible ; resilient enough to absorb shock, so as to reduce vibration, with its consequent annoyance to residents and possible damage to property ; and to secure the minimum amount of wear and tear of vehicles.

10. It must not be too expensive having regard to No. 6, but it can be taken as an axiomatic truth that a cheap road is never an economical proposition.

11. Camber should be so flat that just sufficient cross fall is allowed to enable water to run off to the sides. Flat cambers encourage slow traffic to keep off the middle of the road, and minimize the danger of skidding. When fast traffic is overtaking and passing slower moving vehicles in the centre of the road, crossing over to the opposite side is fraught with danger on most roads.

12. Gradients should never be excessive, and this factor will influence the kinds of materials to be employed in surfacing.

13. Permanence is important so as to obviate the necessity for frequent repairs, and consequent obstruction of traffic and to ensure economy in maintenance.

In addition to traffic resistance, which is offered by gradients, other forces are also in operation, viz. axle friction ; rolling resistance, due to surface irregularities and friction, speed, and wind pressure. If the tractive resistance of dry smooth asphalt be taken as 1, then stone setts will vary from 1·50 to 3, macadam from 2·50 to 8 according to its condition, whether dry, muddy or loose.

FOOTWAYS

The necessity for the provision of suitable and sufficient footways for the use of pedestrians, has, strange to say, been overlooked to a considerable extent in investigating the best types of construction for carriage-ways. In the towns, however, this is not so manifest, but throughout the country the neglect of this provision would seem to indicate that the pedestrian had ceased to exist. It has been laid down by the model by-laws that in roads on which buildings are erected, one-fifth of the carriage-way width shall be dedicated on each side for footways. Owing to the congested condition of the rural roads it is high time that a similar provision for the protection of the way-farer should be afforded, though a footpath may not be necessary on both sides of such highways. In many places, where footways exist, they have been so much neglected or so badly constructed that the pedestrian is compelled to walk on the well-made carriage-way. But the fault is not that of the road-maker, rather is it due to past failures of the authorities—local and central—to earmark essential sums of money for this work in contradistinction to that of carriage-way maintenance.

In both urban and rural areas it is necessary that the footpath shall be 4 to 6 inches at the edge above the channel, to provide a measure of protection from road vehicles which, otherwise, when badly driven, or through defective steering apparatus, might mount the footways to the danger of the pedestrians. All footways should be smooth, with sufficient frictional resistance to avoid slipperiness.

WIDER FOOTWAYS

As carriage-way construction becomes more and more of a permanent character, the demand increases that the various services, such as sewers, drains, gas, water, and electric mains, telegraph and telephone wires, shall be laid under the footways. The inevitable result of this points to the necessity for wider footways than are provided to-day, and this will be a determining factor in deciding the over-all width of a road. Trees which can, at the same time, be both a delight and a nuisance, require thought in footpath design, and a strip at least 3 feet wide should be provided on each footway for this purpose. This strip should never be regarded as part of the footway, but should be specially

dedicated for the purpose of tree planting. All this points
to the necessity for the adoption of a rule which should
require that the two footways, in commercial districts
shall total not less than one-half of the carriage-way
width ; in residential areas, one-third the road width ;
and in rural places one-quarter the width of the roadway ;
the minimum width for the footpath in each case being
10 feet, 7 feet 6 inches, and 5 feet—in the last named
instance for, perhaps, one side only.

PAVING MATERIALS

In commercial, shopping, and non-residential, though
busy urban areas, it is necessary that the footways should
be paved either with natural flagstones, artificial stones, or
in situ cement paving, as appearance, durability, and utility
are essential features for footpaths in such localities. The
thickness of the paving slabs requires a little reflection.
Where bulky merchandise is handled no footway slab
should be less than $2\frac{1}{2}$ inches thick; otherwise it is likely to
become broken by the dropping of heavy articles of com-
merce. In all shopping areas artificial stone paving ought
to be laid on a 3-inch bed of Portland-cement concrete to
prevent damage. In other places a paving 2 inches thick
should be sufficient. It is an economy to use only that class
of natural or artificial flagstones, which can be taken up, redressed, and relaid with the old bed uppermost. In
many residential areas, of a semi-urban character, a well
maintained gravel footpath, if laid on a consolidated bed
of clinker ashes, 4 inches thick, to ensure a foundation
and adequate drainage for surface water, is satisfactory.
It is much more pleasant for walking on than the paved
footways, and affords a pleasant relief for those whose
working days are spent in crowded centres of industry.
Tarred limestone macadam is a suitable material for footpaths, and as it can be painted and gritted from time to
time, it is possible, when this is done, to cover up all the
unsightly patches which mark the sites of openings.

An excellent material for busy areas is a 1-inch coat of asphalt on a 4-inch concrete foundation. In rural areas the demand for footpaths would be met by the provision of a properly shaped footway, of adequate width, surfaced with gravel on a layer of ashes.

PART III: METHODS AND MATERIALS

CHAPTER IX

ROLLERS AND ROLLING

THE first reference to the rolling-in of the loose materials, used in the construction of roads, occurs in the year 1619, but the idea was not put into practical use until 1787. A patent was taken out in 1699 for an invention which is described as "an instrument or engine which will amend and levell the roads."

In no branch of this subject of road making was progress, at one leap, made so manifest as by the invention of the steam road roller. Prior to the introduction of this mechanical device for the rapid consolidation of road foundations and surfacing materials, the traffic had to consolidate its own roadways, a state of affairs which seems to belong to a distant past. Horse-drawn rollers were, however, in use to a limited extent. In the year 1867 the first machine was placed on the roads for rolling in the materials employed in their construction, but several years were required to evolve a successful type, and many more years had to elapse before the steam road roller came into general use. This last-named period was probably in the first decade of the present century. In consequence of the accumulated knowledge of the subject of steam road roller construction several firms have, for many years, been able to meet the demands, and to-day this useful machine, " Made in England," can be found doing most excellent service in the least to be expected places of the world.

WAVINESS

It has been held, and with considerable evidence to prove the indictment, that the steam road roller was responsible for the initial waves which were produced in newly made water-bound roads, which become more pronounced with vehicular traffic. It is well known that if a thickness of more than 4 to 5 inches of hard broken stone is rolled at one operation, the material may be pushed forward by the front roller, and, in this way, the familiar waviness of a road was started. This action was due to the compacting of the stones into ridges, over which the roller rode, to begin again the same kind of operation after leaving the crest of each wave. The late Colonel Crompton, C.B., R.E., who was the doyen of road makers, designed, some years ago, a three-axle roller to overcome this tendency in rolling to wave formation. His idea was to enable the pressure on the road surface to vary, the maximum amount to be exerted on the summit and the minimum on the trough. This was accomplished by mounting the middle roller on springs.

ROAD ROLLING A SKILLED OPERATION

Road rolling is a skilled operation, and the driver of the roller needs to be an experienced man at this class of work to ensure success. After the broken stone for a water bound macadam road has been spread, it is rolled dry before any materials for binding its elements together have been added. As soon as a sufficiently mosaic-like appearance has been obtained, and the stones have ceased to creep under the movements of the roller, the minimum amount of binding material—gravel, screenings from the old road, or stone dust—can be scattered over the surface, and water, about 3 gallons for each square yard applied. A slurry will be produced, and this must be brushed into the interstices as the rolling proceeds, and the bulk of it brushed off in the final stages of the operation. Rolling should be done from the sides towards the centre, and never in the opposite direction.

In recent years there has been a distinct tendency towards a lighter type of roller: 28 years ago a road roller of 12 to 15 tons was regarded as necessary, but to-day a much lighter type of roller is quite sufficient for all purposes, and the tendency is still towards lightness. The heavier type of roller is not required for any form of bituminous, or asphalt paving; consequently the days of the heavy roller are numbered, and the manufacturers have probably realized this important fact.

ROAD ROLLING DATA

To enable calculations to be made of the working capacity of a roller, the following data are necessary—

1. That the number of working days in any year will not, ordinarily, exceed 250.

2. That after working 100 hours the boiler should be washed out, and the engine overhauled.

3. That a roller in good working order should, if uninterrupted, be able to consolidate from 20 to 25 cubic yards of broken stone (macadam) per day of 8 hours for a water bound surface.

4. That a 10-ton roller will be required to pass over the same area from 50 to 75 times to obtain sufficient consolidation. But the number of times will vary with the hardness or softness of the stone employed, and the quantity of binding material used.

5. That one roller is required for the maintenance of each 50 miles of urban road.

6. That the materials required per day for a 10-ton modern type road roller are approximately

Firewood	$1\frac{3}{4}$ lb.
Coal	$3\frac{1}{4}$ cwt.
Oil and stores	

7. Work to be done may be estimated as follows—One cube yard of broken stone should cover 9 yards super of road surface, therefore, each day 200 yards super (the mean of 20 and 25 yards cube), should be consolidated. In this operation, with a 6 feet wide roller, the distance travelled

will be $\frac{200}{2} \times 62$ (the mean of 50 and 75) or 6,200 yards. The average speed of a roller may be taken as $1\frac{1}{2}$ miles per hour; but, as one-third of its time, during actual operations, is occupied in stopping and reversing, the speed per hour will be only one mile; consequently $3\frac{1}{2}$ hours' work is represented, from which it will be possible to calculate the cost per yard super for rolling, allowing 15 per cent on the capital outlay of the roller for interest, depreciation, and maintenance.

PETROL AND DIESEL DRIVEN ROLLERS

These types of roller have become favoured because of their greater convenience and speedier operations. A road roller driven by steam necessitates longer hours for the operator than a petrol driven one, as the time occupied in getting up steam and banking fires can, with a petrol roller, be devoted to actual work of road consolidation.

SCARIFYING

This operation means the breaking up of the surface of an old road to enable it to be reshaped and reformed by the addition of a new coat of stone. The work can be very expeditously performed, by means of mechanical attachments to the roller, at the rate of 100 to 300 square yards per hour. The cost per square yard varies by a very considerable amount according to the class of road, width, and working conditions.

Several forms of scarifiers are in use, some attached directly to the roller and others detached but drawn by the roller. The latter method is to be preferred as it puts less strain on the roller. Owing, however, to the growing employment of bituminous materials, for road-making purposes, the scarifier is becoming less necessary, as at times it is beyond the strength of the lighter powered rollers to break up satisfactorily a well-consolidated road which has been used for a number of years.

Instead of scarifying, the bituminous surface coat may now be removed with the aid of paraffin pressure burners, as the material, after heating, can then be easily stripped by means of a shovel, after which a new topping coat can be expeditiously laid down.

CHAPTER X

WATER BOUND MACADAM

IT is not good to speak ill of the bridge which has carried us over, but there is a tendency in these days of insistent demands for good roads (which have been met by the adoption of scientific principles by the road makers), to despise the water bound method of construction. The fact is overlooked that most of the roads of this country are constructed in this manner, and that for a long time to come this method of construction will continue, because of the use that can be made of local materials and labour, and the resultant low first cost. The water bound macadam road has received a new lease of life by reason of the extensive use which has been made in recent years of tar, bitumen and emulsions for waterproofing the surface, and for holding together the uppermost materials of which such a road is formed. Both these are essential because the penetration of water to the subsoil makes it yield under pressure, and the movement of the road stones causes attrition, which leads to dust or mud according to the climatic conditions. John Loudon McAdam was one of the early pioneers of the system of water bound construction, on a scientific basis. Since his time, the advent of the steam road roller has made it possible to do in a day what formerly took weeks to complete ; but the idea remains that cubical pieces of stone can be made to fit together in a mosaic-like manner to form a running surface for vehicles.

ELEMENTARY IDEAS OF ROAD MAKING

Prior to the introduction of the steam road roller, it was the general practice to spread the broken stone on the road and to compel the traffic, by means of obstructions, to pass over it, and in this way to consolidate the surface. This, though in the days of steel tyres and before the

arrival of the pneumatic-tyred motor vehicles, was a fruitful source of annoyance and danger to all road users.

In consequence of these very elementary principles of
road construction, it became an established idea in the
minds of many of those who constituted the highway
authorities of this country, particularly in rural or semi-
rural areas, that road making could easily be carried out,
provided some stones, earth, simple tools, and the human
element, with sufficient muscular strength, were available.
These ideas no longer exist, and even the construction of
a water bound road is now admitted to demand considerable knowledge, which can only be secured by practical
experience. In the construction of a water bound road,
the Telford method is now universally adopted, and a
foundation provided. On this foundation, smaller stones
are spread to fill up the interstices of the larger stones of
which the foundation is formed. After rolling this base,
an irregular surface is provided, with sufficient key to enable
the wearing coat to combine with it and form a compact
whole. In rolling the surface layer, the broken stones
should not be spread to a greater thickness than 3 to 5
inches, a thickness that will vary between these limits by
the character of the material and weight and capacity of
the roller.

THICKNESS OF ROAD CRUST

To enable a water bound road to resist the destructive
action of heavy traffic, it may be assumed as an axiom
that the foundation should not be less than 9 inches thick,
on a subsoil that has a theoretical bearing capacity of two
tons per square foot, and that this thickness should be
increased as the stability of the subsoil diminishes. Such
being the case, what should be the thickness of the surface
or wearing coat ? As the pressure on the subsoil varies
inversely as the cube of the thickness of the crust (the
combined foundation and wearing coat) and as this pressure
is transmitted in a downward direction in the form of a

WATER BOUND ROAD IN COURSE OF PREPARATION FOR AN ASPHALT WEARING COAT

Note "pot-holes" in road

(Photo: Tecart Studios, London W.C.1)

Water Bound Road on Slope showing Breaking Up of the Surface

(Photo: Tecart Studios, London, W.C.1)

truncated cone, the lines of which diverge from the point of contact with the wheel at an angle of 45°, it is possible to compute the theoretical thickness required. The area of the wheel in contact with the road surface may be assumed to be 9 inches (arc of wheel 3 inches multiplied by width of tyre 3 inches) ; total thickness of crust, 12 inches (9 inches in the foundation, and 3 inches of wearing coat) ; and the load equal to 7,500 lb. per inch of tyre width ; therefore the area of disturbed pressure will be—

B = Base area
T = Thickness of crust
A = Arc of wheel in inches
W = Width of tyre in inches
$B = (2T + A)(2T + W) = 5$ square feet.

As it is expected that any road may at any time be required to withstand a pressure of 10 tons on one rear wheel at point of contact with the road, including impact, it will be seen that this thickness of 12 inches is sufficient, provided that the subsoil has been rendered sufficiently stable. With a subsoil of less bearing capacity it will be noted that either the foundation, or the wearing coat, or both, must be increased in thickness.

CAUSES OF FAILURE

A water bound road often fails under intensive traffic conditions by reason of soft or yielding subsoil, lack of drainage, insufficient foundation, unsuitable broken stone, dirty binding materials, weak haunches, abutments not strong enough to resist lateral pressure, and perviousness of surface. All these items, except the broken stone, are dealt with elsewhere in this book. Stone to be suitable for road work should have the physical qualities of hardness and toughness to resist abrasive action, and durability, a chemical quality, to resist the effects of climate. It should be capable of forming a compact mass under rolling action with the minimum quantity of binding materials.

Prior to the introduction of surface treatment, already referred to, the stones forming a water bound road were held together only by the moisture tension of the finely divided particles between each piece of stone. Consequently, such roads, when not kept daily watered during spells of dry weather, broke up under the action of wheel traffic, to the accompaniment of clouds of dust as the moisture evaporated, and such roads were a constant source of trouble and expense. Surface abrasion and interstitial attrition are continuous processes in this class of road where the surface is unprotected by a coating of tar or bitumen and tar.

Frost plays a destructive part in water bound roads owing to the forces of expansion which are set up. After a severe winter the surface of such roads, however well they may have been protected by tar and bitumen spraying or painting, will be found to present a sieve-like pattern, due to cracks. These cracks allow water to pass through to the foundation with further disastrous results to the road structure.

CHAPTER XI

WOOD PAVING, SETT PAVING, BRICK PAVING

WHEN originally introduced into this country, and for the period between the third and fourth decades of last century, the blocks for a wood-paved road were laid directly on the natural earth bed, without any treatment or preparation whatever. Failures were numerous, but they resulted in improved methods of construction, and ultimately wood paving came to be regarded as one of the best methods for surfacing heavily trafficked roads. In the early days, the hard woods such as Jarrah and Karri, of Australian origin, the English grown oak, ash, elm, and beech, were regarded as suitable timbers for the preparation of wood blocks. But experience proved that these hard woods were not satisfactory, because they did not wear so evenly as the softer varieties for this class of work ; and were more liable to expansion and permanent contraction ; their very hardness and brittleness made the joints more liable to open by the breaking away of the edges under traffic. On the other hand, they were not so easily deformed as the softer woods, and could often be taken up and relaid. Hard wood paving was much more slippery than the softer variety as it polished under the influence of rubber tyres, necessitating the frequent use of sand, grit, and chippings.

The soft wood blocks are obtained chiefly from the timbers grown in northern Europe, belonging to the pine family. These blocks are obtained in several sizes from 7 to 9 inches long, 3 inches wide, and from 4 to 5 inches deep. It is not advisable to use smaller sized blocks, owing to the possibility that they might have been cut out of timber of insufficient growth. Any greater depth than 4 inches is unnecessary, and this difference of one inch between width and depth ensures that all blocks are laid with the grain vertical to the surface.

A block, much used for wood-paving, known by the trade name of "Firmosec," has, before creosoting, a spline of wood fixed along the bottom of one side and end, and two smaller pieces on the same side about three-quarters of an inch from the top, and a groove along the end of the block into which the grouting material can run to minimize the danger of rain water passing to the underside of the paving.

ADVANTAGES

Wood paving for heavy traffic was very popular because of its distinctly resilient properties; and it makes an ideal surface for narrow streets, particularly in residential areas, where the traffic is of an intensive character. To the elastic properties of soft wood blocks is to be attributed the endurance of the paving. On this point, it may be remarked that, in the case of heavily trafficked roads, the expectation of life was about 15 years.

Wood block paving, when properly laid on a sufficient concrete foundation, should normally be inexpensive to maintain, and this quality, in addition to its noiselessness, can be considered one of the greatest advantages of this class of road surface.

Before laying, the wood blocks must have been impregnated with creosote oil at a pressure of 120 to 150 pounds per square inch, after a preliminary treatment in a vacuum at 12 to 15 pounds per square inch to remove moisture and air from the wood cells to enable the preservative to penetrate the whole of the fibres. This process fulfils a twofold purpose, as it arrests the fungoid growths which lead to the decay of timbers, and minimizes any sponge-like action of the blocks to absorb water, and consequent swelling. From 7 to 8 pounds of creosote per cube foot is sufficient, as an excess quantity may be troublesome during the summer months.

DISADVANTAGES

Objections can be raised against the use of wood block paving, as owing to the application of materials to guard against slipperiness of the surface, these roads may become dirty in wet weather, and may be somewhat dusty during dry spells. Prior to the introduction of motor vehicles, unpleasant exhalations were encountered during hot weather, but, with the diminution of horse traffic, this nuisance has disappeared. But the absorbent nature of the wood block remains; and its retention of moisture, (notwithstanding the creosoting process) and the number of joints through which water can pass to the concrete foundation, are matters that cannot be overlooked. During the hot dry months of the year the blocks shrink, the joints open and become filled with grit. When the rain falls there is a tendency for the water to pass to the underside of the blocks, causing them to swell and lift up in patches, technically termed "blisters."

In all cases, wood paving is laid on a concrete foundation, and it is better to lay the blocks directly on to it rather than on a float coat of sand and cement. A difference of opinion existed amongst road makers as to the best method of laying wood paving. The blocks could be close jointed, or space jointed. If the ordinary spaced jointed method of laying is adopted, splines $\frac{1}{8}$ inch wide are inserted between each row of blocks and removed; pitch and tar, or a special grouting material is then run into the joint. As an alternative method laths one-tenth of an inch wide, and 1 inch deep, to separate row from row, could be inserted and not removed, but kept in position to give the necessary width of joint for grouting purposes.

In laying the blocks, it was usual to place three courses parallel with the kerb, on each side, but in the road the courses run at right angles to the kerbs. Sometimes the blocks were laid diagonally, at an angle of 60°, but this necessitated much cutting.

Excessive camber had to be guarded against, as it could

be a contributory cause of the lifting or blistering during periods of heavy rain following a drought.

EXPANSION OF WOOD BLOCKS

As the expansion of a wood paved road may be from 1·50 to 1·75 per cent, it is necessary to make sufficient provision for this, otherwise the kerbs and footpaths would suffer. Well-puddled clay, when used for expansion joints, was laid contiguous to, and parallel with, the kerbs. If the width of this joint exceeded 1½ inches it was likely to be troublesome owing to disturbances by the wheels of vehicles.

When wood paving is laid with close joints, more trouble is to be expected from expansion than in the case of spaced blocks, the joints of which are filled with a bituminous mixture.

It is sound practice, the third day after completion, to roll into the wood blocks as much ⅜ inch crushed ballast as possible, which armours the surface and affords an excellent foothold for horses.

Wood paved roads are treated, from time to time, with a suitable preparation for sealing the joints. This is applied either as a hot mixture or as a cold emulsion; and possibly there is much to be said in favour of the latter owing to its lower viscosity, which enables it to run more easily into the joints.

SETT PAVING

More than one hundred years ago McAdam, when at the zenith of his fame (in 1827 he was appointed Surveyor General to the Commissioners of Metropolitan Turnpike Roads), stated that he regarded the paving of streets with stone setts as a "desperate remedy," and complained, on many occasions, that the Trusts had, at great expense, "imported stone from Scotland" for this purpose. Telford, on the other hand, was in favour of paving, and setts were used by him in three ways, viz.: (1) over the entire width of the road; (2) in the centre only; (3) along both sides of the road. In the last two methods named, the remaining portion was surfaced with broken stone. Experience, gained throughout the years that have since elapsed, has proved that Telford was right, for without this class of paving it would have been impossible to carry the heavy traffic which, since the advent of the industrial era, has been so intense in the vicinity of docks and railway sidings, and in many thoroughfares where similar conditions have existed.

The setts which were generally used for paving were of granite from several British sources, but large quantities were imported from Norway and Sweden. In the North of England, whinstone setts were used, but they are apt to become very slippery. In parts of Yorkshire and Lancashire, a hard sandstone or grit sett was employed with considerable advantage, as it affords an excellent foothold for horses. Granite setts range in size from 3 inch cubes to those of various lengths, but a sett longer than 6 or 7 inches is not often used. The width generally is from 3 to 4 inches, and the depth from 5 to 7 inches. The chief points to be borne in mind with regard to sett paving are: (1) that each parcel of setts shall be of equal quality throughout; (2) that they shall conform to a calliper test, and that the maximum deviation in any specified size shall not exceed $\frac{1}{4}$ inch in either depth or breadth; and (3) that the dressing shall be sufficient to ensure squareness on each face, and (4) that each opposite side shall be parallel throughout, which denotes that setts with bulges or hollows are unsuitable.

It was usual to allow random lengths up to a limit of 2 inches, provided that an agreed percentage was not exceeded.

This type of paving, since the perfecting of bituminous forms of road surfaces, and owing partly to its high initial cost, is much less used nowadays than in former years.

METHOD OF LAYING

Formerly the tendency in sett paving was in the direction of large joints, which were supposed to afford a better foothold for horses ; and these joints were grouted with bitumen, pitch, or cement and sand, after filling or " racking " the joints with $\frac{1}{8}$ to $\frac{3}{8}$ inch clean chippings, which could be automatically packed by careful ramming of the setts. The changing character of the traffic has led to the demand for a better dressed type of sett, to secure a finer joint, as it was discovered that the wheels of rapid moving heavy vehicles, when fitted with rubber tyres, cause a partial vacuum to be formed, which sucks out the jointing materials. In places where wide jointed sett paving occurs, this trouble can, to a large extent, be obviated by giving the setts a coating of pitch or tar, and a dressing with chippings, which provides an excellent foot grip for horses, and improves the running of motor vehicles.

Setts were invariably laid on a bed of concrete, though, on the Continent, remarkably serviceable *pavé* exists where the setts are laid on a sand bed only. Prior to the introduction of the heavy traffic with which we are to-day so familiar, the concrete foundations for paving rarely exceeded 6 inches in depth, but this is now insufficient, and the concrete is either made deeper or steel reinforcing is introduced to strengthen the material.

It is an economic advantage to lay deeper types of setts, as they can be taken up, redressed, and used again. In this way they have a double life. If this is taken into consideration when sett paving works are decided upon, and the estimated life of the sett divided into the cost per yard super, it will be found that a great economy is effected by using the very best type of sett that can be purchased.

In laying setts on a concrete foundation, it is usual to interpose a $1\frac{1}{2}$ inch to 2 inch layer of sand to act as a cushion to distribute throughout the grains the destructive stresses set up in this rigid type of road surface.

DISADVANTAGES

The great objection to sett paving is, that owing to its rigidity, it is extremely noisy ; but with closer joints this unsatisfactory feature can be considerably reduced. For this reason the road maker has insisted upon a much superior type of dressing, and with the closer joints which are possible, a simple bituminous grouting only is required. Close joints ensure the minimum of wear. With the old kind of sett paving, the arrises of each stone soon became worn or damaged by abrasion, and resulted in the jolting and bumping of traffic, which was so fruitful a cause of noise and vibration.

" DURAX " PAVING

Germany was the home of a system of paving known in this country as " Durax." The setts are small, $2\frac{1}{2}$ or 3 inches, of not quite parallel sides, which, when laid, enable an arch, or rather a fan shape, to be developed. This type of paving is sound in principle, and is not noisy, but has not been used to any great extent in this country. It has been successfully employed on old water bound macadam roads, where it was necessary to strengthen the surface without incurring a large expenditure of money.

BRICK PAVING

Although bricks, for the paving of carriage-ways, have not been used to any extent in this country, a reference to the subject must be made. It has been argued by some that bricks would make a suitable surfacing material for heavily trafficked roads, and the promoters of this idea refer to American practice.

It is somewhat unfortunate that America, the land of innovations, should be used in support of this claim, as the conditions there are very different from those which appertain in this country.

Bricks for paving footpaths have long been in use here, but have fallen into disfavour since the introduction of the artificial stone slab.

Bricks for carriage-ways must have similar characteristics to those which distinguish a suitable stone for sett paving, and these are not easy to produce by any known synthetic process. It is hardly necessary to say that no ordinary building brick would meet the demands; consequently a paving brick for surfacing a carriage-way must be specially made for the purpose. The well-known blue bricks of this country have been used, but these, subjected to ordinary traffic, have been known to fail under crushing action.

In common with all other paving materials, it is essential that a brick paved carriage-way should have a sufficient foundation. This term " sufficient " is very wide and varies with every case. In some places, the natural sub-soil might be sufficient ; in others, an old water bound macadam surface, if levels permit, might suffice ; whilst a more or less unstable foundation might be improved by incorporating sand with it.

A serious defect in this type of paving arises from the varying quality of the bricks, a condition of things inseparable from this class of material; otherwise several advantages could be claimed for this method of carriage-way surfacing.

Whatever kind of foundation is provided, it is usual to lay the bricks on a sand bed of from 1 to 2 inches in depth, for the same reasons as have already been described under sett paving.

The jointing of the bricks can be the same as for setts, but bitumen is to be preferred as it does not crack, and furnishes a medium for the expansion and contraction of the materials. Further, as economy must be considered, it is possible with either sand or bitumen grouting to take up and relay the bricks, or at least a high percentage of them, which is not easy of accomplishment when cement is used for jointing. Unless a sealed joint is provided, trouble will result from the passage of water to the subsoil. Sand is ineffective in this respect, and, as it furnishes little frictional resistance, tractive effort is considerably increased.

CHAPTER XII

CONCRETE

WITH Portland cement and suitable aggregates, the road maker is provided with materials which enable him to design suitable and sufficient foundations. The advantages may be stated to be—

1. That it is possible to calculate the thickness required with more certainty than for a foundation formed of hardcore.

2. That a monolithic homogeneous mass provides for an even distribution of load.

3. It is possible, by means of steel reinforcing materials, to resist the various stresses and strains which tend to diminish the efficiency of every kind of foundation.

The disadvantages are—

1. That in first cost a concrete foundation may be an expensive item, if a suitable aggregate is not available locally.

2. That although it can be relied upon in places where the subsoil has a low bearing value, or in areas where the traffic is heavy and intensive, the same results may often be obtained by other and cheaper means.

3. That it does not permit of such easy access to the subsoil, when trenches have to be opened, as a hardcore foundation. In places where single reinforcement is used this trouble is doubled, and where double reinforcement exists, the labour involved in opening out such a road is quadrupled.

4. It is less resilient than rolled stone or an old water bound crust, when such a road can be used as a foundation for a bituminous wearing surface.

5. It reacts more readily, because of its rigidity to stresses and strains which are set up by traffic conditions and climatic changes.

6. That as a period of from two to three weeks should elapse, during which time the concrete must be protected from sun and wind to ensure slow hardening, this delay makes concrete foundations difficult to provide in business centres. With rapid hardening cements, three to five days is a sufficient period for the necessary chemical processes to be completed; but by using a special cement the time can be reduced to 24 hours.

The aggregate for this class of work generally consists of four parts hard stone, broken from $1\frac{1}{2}$ inches to $\frac{3}{16}$ inch; two parts of clean sharp sand; and one part of Portland cement. The ordinary gravel is not always to be recommended owing to its water worn and rounded properties; but if crushed and washed it becomes a useful aggregate. In the mixing much skill is necessary, and only the minimum amount of water should be used; any slight excess over 20 gallons per yard cube reduces the strength of the concrete very considerably. This is required for concrete where the aggregate is broken washed gravel; in the case of a lime-stone aggregate the volume of water would be 33 per cent in excess of that stated. Concrete should never be laid when the temperature is below freezing point; and during periods of frost, all freshly laid materials must be carefully protected. Tamping or ramming is a necessary process, as soon as the concrete is placed in position, to expel air bubbles and to secure density; but care must be exercised, as excessive tamping will weaken the mass in wet mixes by causing the finer particles, composing the mortar or matrix, to be brought to the surface, leaving the bottom stones devoid of the essential cementitious materials.

The presence of water in the subsoil must be guarded against by means of drainage. The bearing capacity may be increased by means of a 3 to 6 inch consolidated bed of clinker ashes, which also acts as an insulating coat. With efficient drainage and compacting the subsoil should be able to carry at least 2 tons per square foot, and on this basis the calculations can be made.

CONCRETE SLAB

In order to provide for the free movement of the concrete slab, this bed of ashes, if used (but the use is not recommended), should be brought to a smooth surface; and although the resistance to movement will be considerable, the tensile strength of the concrete should overcome it, but the length of the slab must not be too great, without the provision of an expansion joint. In practice, special waterproof paper is often placed under the concrete slab: to reduce excessive loss of moisture; to prevent the escape of cement into the base or subgrade; to reduce friction between the slab and the base; to prevent deleterious materials from becoming mixed with the concrete; and to reduce the risk of attack of the concrete by chemicals carried in the subsoil water. The most important factor to be observed in the calculations is that the concrete must be thick enough so to distribute the pressure, due to the maximum impact shocks, that the subsoil shall not be stressed beyond its elastic limits. It may be assumed that the pressure on any road surface is radially transmitted through an angle of 45° to the supporting subsoil; consequently, the thicker the concrete, the greater the area of subsoil likely to be disturbed. The area of contact of a wheel with the road surface is from 8 to 9 square inches, and as one of the rear wheels is capable of exerting a force of 10 tons, this may easily mean 170 tons per square foot, which is not excessive with properly graded and mixed concrete. The area of the subsoil over which this pressure is distributed, from the apex of the truncated cone at a loaded point on the road surface, may be assumed to be 5 square feet. As the point load is taken at 10 tons, the intensity of pressure will be 2 tons per square foot on the subsoil, which is rarely exceeded on a smooth surfaced road. But this furnishes no factor of safety, and as road transport ever tends to increase in volume, speed, and weight, it is evident that a thickness of 6 inches is inadequate for modern heavily trafficked roads, though quite sufficient to stand up to the demands of suburban street traffic.

As the supporting capacity of the material increases in proportion to the square of the thickness, it is obvious that a foundation of concrete can economically be made to carry heavier loads.

REINFORCED FOUNDATIONS

In recent years, much attention has been given to the subject of reinforced concrete foundations, with a view to increasing the strength of the slab, so as to reduce its thickness to render it, as a consequence, more resilient, and to cheapen the cost. The presence of a suitable reinforcing material should increase the resistance moment and thus enable the thickness to be decreased, thereby effecting an economy. The question of resiliency is worthy of the closest attention, as rigid foundations are destructive of road surfaces; and the forces of reaction tend equally towards excessive wear and tear of the vehicles. A reinforced concrete foundation should provide that element of elasticity necessary to enable the concrete in which it is employed to resist, without fracture, the impact shocks of heavy traffic and the forces of expansion and contraction which are set up by changing temperatures.

In consequence of the complicated stresses and strains in the concrete, both top and bottom reinforcements may be necessary in places where the subsoil is treacherous. Clay, for example, is liable to so wide a range of volumetric change, that its lifting power can be destructively used where it cannot expand except in an upward direction. In such circumstances, transverse contraction joints must be provided. In places where the subsoil can expand and contract in all directions, expansion or contraction joints are unnecessary, but the concrete may be carried 18 inches beyond the channel, on each side of the road, to prevent the possibility of any deformation of the alignment of the kerbs, and to secure a wider distribution of forces. This method, however, is not general in practice as the kerbs are laid on the slab. In all places where the concrete is surfaced with wood blocks, asphalt, or bituminous materials, it will be realized that double reinforcement may generally be unnecessary, and single reinforcement only be required. But the decision must depend upon the amount and weight of traffic and the type of subgrade.

One of the arguments in favour of using reinforcement is that if 600 lb. per square inch represents its power of resisting compression, and only 60 lb. for tension, unreinforced concrete is only performing a part of its possible useful work.

EXPANSION AND CONTRACTION

A slab of concrete 100 feet long and one foot wide may, in setting, contract 0·625 of an inch; and a further 0·375 of an inch for every 50° F. fall in temperature; or will expand *pro rata* for an equal rise in temperature; in other words, the expansion and contraction of concrete are equal in all directions. It will thus be noted that temperature plays an important part in this class of work, and if the materials are mixed during a period of low temperature, above freezing point, contraction will be excessive in the process of setting. Concrete sets slowly when the temperature falls below 50° F. After setting it will expand when wet and contract when dry; and such an alternating sequence, as may easily occur in a road bed, may lead to ultimate expansion. The necessity for an impervious road surface is evident.

Theoretically such an expansion would be possible due to moisture absorption, but as the road dries the temperature rises and the shrinkage caused by the drying out of the road is partially counteracted by the expansion due to temperature.

When single reinforcement is employed, it is generally placed 2 inches below the surface, and no points of destructive contraflexure stresses should occur if the load is properly distributed over the subsoil to prevent undue deflection. The principle of the loaded beam is applied, in which tension occurs in the lower third of the depth. Owing to the high compressive nature of concrete, there is no necessity to provide for this, in ordinary cases, by placing the reinforcement nearer the surface. Contraflexure stresses are, however, set up by two heavy vehicles standing or passing each other at a short distance apart. The reaction to load pressure is obtained by the distribution of the forces, and the resistance of the ground outside the base of the cone, which supports the point load of the wheel of a vehicle.

Although it is possible to provide a concrete foundation of sufficient thickness to make deflection negligible, and thus prevent the setting up of any contraflexure stresses, it is not always economical to do so. In those places where the traffic demands are such that unreinforced concrete is insufficient, it is an economy to use reinforcement, rather than to increase the thickness.

SURFACE REINFORCING

The use of single light reinforcing fabric at 2 inches from the surface is effective for resisting temperature changes, and can be advantageously used for this purpose in all cases where load distribution over the bed is provided by means of a firm subsoil. The loads on a road are always concentrated, and although they are distributed over a considerable area, there is a resulting upward pressure, which induces tensional strains at the surface of the concrete. Whilst allowing for the possibility of a series of hair cracks, such a dissipation of initial stresses is much to be preferred to the provision of expansion and contraction joints, or the possibility of the occurrence of large cracks which always extend to the surface or wearing coat, when formed of asphalt. Both joints and cracks are possible channels for the conveyance of rain-water to the base. Water weakens the bearing capacity of the subsoil, causes the oxidization of the steel reinforcing fabric and consequent loss as a stress resisting agency. In addition to limiting the destructive effects due to temperature changes at the surface of the concrete, top reinforcement resists contraflexure or opposing stresses, and the damage which may result to the surface due to tension and shear set up by the tractive effort of wheels and particularly those of self-propelled vehicles. This remark would appear to have reference to concrete running surfaces only, but it has a wider application as it has become the practice to prepare the concrete foundation and leave it as a wearing coat, for a varying period of time, before applying a resilient wearing surface.

In the use of some types of asphalt paving for town roads—those roads which may have to be opened up for many municipal purposes and which are subjected to intense traffic conditions—the use of Portland cement concrete for the preparation of a suitable foundation is essential. All roads do not, however, present these conditions and, in consequence, it is necessary to prescribe different foundations and wearing surfaces for different types of roads. A whole concrete road may fail to meet the demands of modern heavy, high speed traffic if it is too rigid, and, if too rigid, its structure must in consequence suffer from the repeated sledge-hammer-like blows which descend upon it by impact shocks. The unceasing regularity of traffic vibration, whether large or small, has very destructive tendencies which demonstrate well-known truths in mechanics and physics. Many whole concrete roads have, however, proved that they are capable of resisting the destructive effects of modern heavy and high speed traffic.

DOUBLE REINFORCEMENT

An exhaustive study of this subject will probably reveal the fact that the more resilient the foundation, the longer will be the life of the road ; consequently, double reinforcement may play an important part, because it will entail less thickness of concrete, and a higher elasticity. Double reinforcement is generally used where roads are carried over peat, bogs, recent excavations, reclamations, and in soils of a high water content and capillarity. This method of construction demands the most minute attention, as only the minimum of reaction can be expected from the subsoil, the bearing capacity of which may, in some cases, have no value whatever, owing to the weakening effect of water. In the laying of steel reinforcing material, sufficient care is not always exercised in keeping the fabric at an even depth, or in securing, by careful filling, the maximum adhesion between the concrete and the steel. In double reinforcing, this weakness can become very manifest, owing to the much more complicated structural arrangement. It is better not to place the reinforcing material at or near the neutral axis, and useless to lay it on the ground. Both of these methods may be pursued, as following the line of least resistance, if the work is not well supervised.

The formula of Professor H. Adams, M.Inst.C.E., is a useful one—

W = Maximum wheel load in tons
w = Average resistance of foundation in tons per square foot
d = Depth in inches from surface of concrete to centre of reinforcement

$$d = \sqrt{4 \cdot 5 \times \frac{W}{w}}$$

Most of the prepared steel fabrics, for reinforcing concrete foundations, have been based on a safe working stress of 600 lb. per square inch for concrete in compression, and 25,000 lb. tension per square inch for the steel. Consequently, the percentage of steel to concrete is very low, and runs from 0·25. It is difficult to calculate the exact amount required with absolute precision, but the necessary calculations can be made, within the limits of safety, by applying the same principles which govern the internal stresses of a beam to determine the maximum limit of tension and compression in the road foundation.

CHAPTER XIII

CONCRETE ROADS

In consequence of the multiplicity of counsellors, and the many opinions which are expressed on the merits and demerits of the various systems of road construction, it is not always an easy matter for the road maker to decide on the type of road best suited to the worst conditions.

Several important highways, entirely of concrete, have been built, and the knowledge of this subject, based on both practical and academic experience, is growing. In the development of building estates concrete roads have completely altered the old methods, and such roads are often constructed before a single house is erected. It has become a practice so to fix the level of the concrete roads, that, should the surfaces at any time show signs of attrition, it would be possible to lay asphalt or other bituminous type of resilient carpet or paving on the concrete.

RESILIENCY

In considering the pros and cons of this part of the subject of road making, that aspect of it which deals with resiliency must be borne in mind. Resiliency is desirable to prevent the damage by vibration of both vehicles and roads, and it has to be furnished either in both or in the vehicle alone. Reinforced concrete, of the minimum possible thickness, can be designed to meet traffic demands, and furnish the springiness required in the structure. The absorption of vibration may be obtained by the provision of a resilient paving on the concrete, and the problem is rendered easy of solution, when the three parts—the bed, the foundation, and the wearing coat—each help to distribute the forces of rolling and impact.

As the construction of a whole concrete road or foundation requires that traffic shall be diverted for a considerable period, the time factor need not be considered, although, in trading centres, it is a serious item. On some roads, however, the width may be sufficient to enable half to be kept open for traffic. When a concrete road has been decided upon, it may not be necessary to excavate lower than the depth required for shaping the underbed to the correct gradients and section.

Concrete can be sufficiently reinforced to meet all the demands that will be made upon it, provided that the subgrade is thoroughly compacted and the subsoil drainage is adequate. If, however,.the subsoil is suspected, in whole or part, of being unstable, it would be necessary to roll in hard core in those sections which might yield under load pressure.

If ashes are ever used as an insulating coat, and any doubt should exist about the presence of sulphates in the ashes, a test should be carried out. If the ashes are kept well watered, however, for a few days before use, the danger of calcium sulphate crystallization (due to capillary attraction) in the mass of the concrete would be reduced. Should a subsoil be sulphate charged an effective protection is provided by a layer of tar one-tenth of an inch thick, and the use of an aluminous cement.

ADVANTAGES

The concrete road presents a low resistance to tractive effort, which results in fuel economy; and generally, a non-absorbent surface, with a flat camber, which reduces the chances of side slip. On curves, super elevation or banking can be easily obtained; and it is possible to make this provision in a concrete foundation which has to carry a wearing coat of other materials. An economical form of construction is possible in districts which furnish a suitable ballast, and this class of material may be used in the wearing surface.

METHODS OF CONSTRUCTION

Two types of construction are generally adopted, viz. one-course and two-course work. In one-course work, the aggregate or ballast, should be properly graded. In this method the concrete can be mixed in the proportions of three to five stone, and one and a half to two and a half sand, and one cement. This class of construction is suitable for roads which have to carry the lighter types of traffic. Two-course concrete roads can be designed to carry heavy traffic, but it is quite a common practice to lay concrete to a depth of from 7 to 9 inches in one coat. The lower course should be mixed in the proportions of one part cement, two parts sand, and four to five parts stone. On this bed, before setting action of the cement is complete, the wearing surface can be laid. The grading of the aggregates for this course varies with practice and traffic needs—3 to $4\frac{1}{2}$ parts of granite and sand to 1 of cement is a common quantitative mixture. But grading is essential, as the greater the density the stronger will be the finished work. To secure this, the coarse aggregate should be composed of three grades of stone, but no material should be used which is not retained on a $\frac{1}{4}$ inch mesh. The sizes will therefore range from $1\frac{1}{2}$ inch, the middle grade being that class of material which will pass a 1 inch screen, and be retained on a mesh of $\frac{1}{2}$ inch. The sand should be such that it will all pass a $\frac{3}{16}$ inch mesh sieve, which size demarcates the coarse aggregates from the sand. Twenty per cent of this sand should pass a No. 50 sieve, of which not more than 10 per cent should be able to pass a No. 100 sieve. Mechanical mixing is to be preferred to hand turning.

WATER FOR MIXING

In the application of clean water, that is to say water free from vegetable matter, the minimum required to secure the wetting of the surfaces of all the particles should be aimed at. The coarser the sand, the less water will be wanted. Fine sand contains more particles;

consequently more water will be required for wetting it, and therefore too fine a sand should be avoided as excess water delays hardening. When the mixed concrete is beaten with a tamper, if the correct volume of water has been added, only the slightest moisture should appear on the surface. Sea water may be used for this purpose, but it delays the final setting of the cement and is not recommended. For successful work it is necessary to ensure that clean materials shall not be spoiled by dirt, or careless and unskilful handling. When water is mixed with the materials for forming the concrete it does not in any way injure the steel reinforcing, owing to the absence of free oxygen, and the presence of caustic lime, which is developed in the setting of the cement. Water, however, which may penetrate through cracks in the concrete, conveys free oxygen and oxidization of the steel reinforcing ensues. For this reason slag or coke breeze ought not to be used when reinforcement is required. Aggregates, in the presence of steel, should be non-porous. Slag often contains pumice and free lime, which causes blowing. Sulphur and ammonia may also be present in slag and coke breeze, and each is detrimental to cement. Porous aggregates also have a low resistance to compression, and are apt to crumble under pressure.

CONTINUOUS AND ALTERNATE BAYS

Two methods of laying the concrete are recognized, known as " continuous " and " alternate bay " construction. If only half the width of a road can be closed at one time the construction in concrete will necessitate a longitudinal joint, and transverse ones, which may be either at right angles with the kerb line or at an angle of about 60° with it. The idea which underlies the last-named method, and which is not recommended, is that two wheels of the same vehicle shall not fall on the same slab at the same moment, but that the load shall be borne by two slabs. The advantages of this method are now regarded as slight. As concrete in setting is known to contract to an exent which varies with temperatures, and other factors, such as density of mass, this alternate bay method of construction has much to commend it. Particularly is this the case if larger bays are made to alternate with a bay of a narrower width, which enables the maximum amount of initial contraction, and the ultimate maxima of expansion, to occur in every alternate bay. Thus it is possible to calculate what the variations due to expansion and contraction shall be in each slab in comparison with the adjoining one. As the maximum stresses will, after about two weeks, have become stabilized over the whole area by the larger bays, only the minimum forces of expansion and contraction will have to be allowed for in the narrower bays.

TAMPING AND FACING

The concrete, as soon as it is laid, must be thoroughly, though not too severely, tamped, an operation which can be performed at the same time as the camber is being developed. The scum, or laitance, which is brought to the surface of the concrete, is formed by the vibratory act of tamping, an action which should be done as rhythmically as possible. The face of the concrete can be finished as desired, but smoothness is not always essential and is not recommended. If smoothness, however, is required a useful way to obtain this is to pass a belt of coarse canvas over the surface from side to side. Although a surface free from cracks can be obtained by the alternate bay method of construction, the many transverse joints which occur are a source of trouble and annoyance as they require constant attention. Bitumen can be used to prevent abrasion of the edges, and the displacement of the aggregate, but it is apt to extrude. Immediately on completion of the work, a layer of sand, not less than one inch thick, should be spread and kept moist by watering, the extent and frequency of which will be controlled by the climatic conditions which prevail at the time. This should be continued for ten days, and the road ought not to be opened for traffic until three weeks have elapsed unless rapid-setting cements are used. Frost, and the direct rays of the midsummer sun, or a drying wind at any season of the year, have a deleterious effect on setting concrete, and should be guarded against by straw or matting.

SURFACE HARDENING

Calcium chloride has been used for accelerating the setting of the concrete to enable traffic to be turned on to it more quickly than by the ordinary method of slow setting and hardening. Practice has proved that this can be done, and traffic allowed to pass over the road fourteen days after completion of the work. If weather conditions are favourable, $2\frac{1}{2}$ lb. of granulated salt, free from lumps, to the square yard may be spread evenly over the surface. Calcium or sodium chloride have high hydroscopic properties and it is supposed that, if this salt is spread in a thin layer over a new concrete road, it penetrates the minute cracks or channels to some depth, and by this means secures the retention of sufficient moisture, and the complete hydration of the cement. Experience has proved that much damage can be done to concrete roads through the spreading of salt on the surface in frosty weather. It is recommended that when salt is spread to counteract frost action it should be mixed with at least four times its volume of granular material. Sea water, when used in cement concrete work, hastens the initial, though it retards the final setting, but should ensure greater ultimate strength. It may have an injurious effect on any exposed reinforcing materials, but the chance of damage in road construction work from this cause is so remote as to be negligible.

Painting with silicate of soda, though seldom done to-day, was reputed to harden the surface of the concrete to a depth of $\frac{1}{4}$ inch, if done as specified by those who supply this chemical. After laying the concrete, the surface must be covered to a depth of one inch with sand, which must be kept wet for ten days. At the end of this period, and after the wet sand has been removed and the surface has dried, a solution, by volume four of water to one silicate of soda, is applied by means of a watering cart or sprinkling cans. After 24 hours, and again after 48 hours, the process should be repeated. On each occasion the solution must be moved backward and forward over the surface with soft brooms.

The surface of the finished concrete road may be treated with one of the heavier forms of road surface dressings, of which many are on the market. By this process it is possible to reduce, very considerably, the abrasive action of wheeled traffic on a concrete surface. This method gives to a concrete road the appearance of an asphalt or tar macadam road, though without the resilient advantages which any form of bituminous material provides when used in entire construction or as a wearing surface only.

EXPANSION JOINTS

Expansion joints have received the consideration which the importance of the subject demands, but there is a wide difference of opinion on the matter. Some road makers deem them unnecessary on the ground that when provided they cause more ultimate trouble than the risks they are supposed to guard against. They certainly cannot be altogether depended upon to prevent the setting up of the stresses which lead to cracks. When surface reinforcing materials are used, the danger of serious cracks is considerably reduced, as a number of superficial hair-like fissures is to be expected, instead of one or more large cracks throughout the full depth of the concrete.

REINFORCING

The reinforcing of a whole concrete road may be necessary in all cases where the subsoil is other than a compact gravel and sand, and the point to determine is whether the reinforcement should be single or double. The use of any kind of steel reinforcement for strengthening concrete is to be advocated, on the ground that not only is economy in the cost of construction ensured, but it enables the thickness to be reduced, and ensures a greater resiliency in the road structure. Generally, when single reinforcement is used, it is laid 2 inches from the surface of the concrete, and in this position it takes up the tension stresses, which concrete unaided can resist to the extent of 60 lb. to the square inch only. It is evident that much more care and experience are necessary in the construction of a whole concrete road than in the preparation of a concrete foundation to carry a wearing surface. When a wearing coat of materials other than concrete is provided, the stresses set up by temperature changes are absorbed at the surface. The steel fabric, of which the reinforcement is formed, should be laid longitudinally, and continuity should be obtained by securely binding together 18 inches overlap in each length of the fabric.

DISADVANTAGES

Perhaps the low resistance to tension possessed by unreinforced concrete is one of its greatest defects, owing to the destruction which is caused by the shearing force of the driving wheels of self-propelled vehicles. The other disadvantages of this method of construction may be summarized as being due to the minimum of resiliency, and the destructive reaction on road vehicles; the expense of repairs and traffic delays; the trouble of reaching underground services; the difficulty of locating water and gas leaks from mains; the abrasion by the feet of horses; and the noise which may be a nuisance to the residents whose houses abut upon the road, and whose property may be damaged by continuous vibrations set up by heavy, rapid-moving, self-propelled vehicles. But, as this objection can be raised, more or less, against all other forms of road construction, it is essential, in the pursuit of an ideal form of road surfacing, that all the facts should be borne in mind.

In the construction of concrete roads, by means of mechanical plant, great progress has been made in recent years, thus expediting construction and cheapening cost.

To deal with all these developments is beyond the purview of this book. Vibrating plant has almost completely eclipsed the older methods of hand-tamping for large undertakings.

British-made machines are available for all classes of concrete road construction, and because of the scarcity and cost of labour, machines for the batching and mixing, transporting, spreading, compacting, and finishing of the materials have been developed.

CHAPTER XIV

RESILIENCY—SPECIFIC GRAVITY— PENETRATION—VISCOSITY— ELASTICITY

THESE terms constantly present themselves to the notice of the road maker; therefore, as this book is primarily intended for the use of students, it is advisable to discuss each term before methods of construction are further considered. The resilient plastic and waterproof character-istics of bitumen and tar, in addition to cementitious qualities, are the chief causes of their resistance to the wear and tear of any road in which they are used as a matrix for binding or holding together the aggregates. The types of aggregate, however, will not be discussed as these in no way affect the points under consideration.

VALUE OF BITUMEN

Bituminous materials continue to play an increasingly important part in the solution of the road problem. They furnish the resilient properties which are required both in base and wearing courses. By their nature they waterproof the surface and prevent any internal movement and conse-quent interstitial wear, which is so fruitful a cause of the disintegration of any class of road where the elements of " dryness " and non-elasticity of particles are inherent. Such faults can be acquired by climatic conditions, as in the case of waterbound roads; and they exist where any improperly graded or consolidated materials, whether based on bitumen, or tar, or both, have been used.

In this system of construction, the whole tendency is ever in the direction of non-rigidity. By proper load distribution, springing, and tyring of vehicles, and in road construction by a correct adjustment of the burden be-tween the subgrade and the resilient surfacing layer, the vehicle designer and road maker have, in co-operation, advanced the science of this subject to a considerable extent.

RESILIENT OR NON-RESILIENT ROADS

To give an answer to the very practical question, so often propounded : " Which gives the most serviceable and durable carriage-way—the rigid or non-rigid foundation ? " —is difficult because it is necessary to reply that each, according to circumstances, is more serviceable and durable than the other. In the case of a water bound road, a rigid foundation would mean the very early destruction of the structure, due to vibration and impact shocks. A rigid foundation is not essential for any kind of tar-macadam road. A hard core foundation, well consolidated, on a dry substratum, provides a most excellent foundation, with sufficient resiliency, but can be objected to on other grounds which are elsewhere considered in this book.

WHERE A NON-RESILIENT FOUNDATION IS NECESSARY

If the underbed of a road consists of wet clay, peat, or any material which contains moisture, or has the capacity of retaining by capillary attraction large quantities of water; or in towns where the roads have been honeycombed for many purposes; or raised by the domestic refuse of many generations; a reasonably rigid foundation is required. If, on the other hand, the substratum has not been disturbed, is dry, resilient, and the ultimate loads will not tax it beyond its elastic limits, a non-rigid foundation can, with advantage, be used. In laying granite setts, for the paving of heavily trafficked roads, we have a striking example of both these influences at work. A concrete rigid foundation is laid, the surface (the setts) are hard and unyielding, therefore, between the two a layer of sand is interposed to act as a cushion. This cushion prevents

the fracture of the granite setts by the mechanical distribution of destructive forces through the medium of the
sand particles. This operation is akin to the resiliency
which must be provided for in the types of road referred
to under the conditions that have been enumerated.

SPECIFIC GRAVITY

With specific gravity, or the density of a substance
relative to water, we are all familiar. It was Archimedes
who discovered that the pressure of a fluid on a body,
suspended in it, acts vertically upwards through the centre
of gravity, and is equal to the weight of the displaced
liquid. The knowledge of this truth enables many useful
tests to be applied; and in road making those materials
which do not comply with predetermined requirements
(the resultant of practice) should be rejected. In the
class of work under consideration, density and homogeneity
are important factors. It is interesting to note the approximate specific gravities of the following materials—

Asphaltic bitumen (from petroleum) . . .	1·00–1·05
Bermudez asphalt	1·06
Cuban ,, ...	1·30
Trinidad (Epuré) asphalt . . .	1·40
Prepared tar No. 1, British Standard specifi-	
cation	1·140–1·225
Prepared tar No. 2, British Standard specifi-	
cation	1·150–1·240

PENETRATION

When an endeavour is made to find out something further
about bitumens and tars, we are confronted by the tech-
nicalities of " Penetration " and " Viscosity." Now what
exactly is meant by these terms, and when and under what
conditions are they used ? Tar, because it is commercially
dealt with as a body that can be made to flow in all directions, is tested for " viscosity " ; but asphalts and bitumens,
which are more solid, are tested for their consistency or
hardness by " penetration." With these, viscosity or
penetration methods of test depend upon the consistency of

the sample to be dealt with. If the material is too soft to allow of the penetration test it is tested for viscosity. When it is desired to ascertain the hardness of any bitumen or asphalt it is determined by means of a machine known as a penetrometer. The penetrations vary with the different sources of supply and methods of production. Further, the consistency, hardness, or penetration, varies with the type of pavement required, and is altered by means of fluxing agents, to meet the various traffic demands and known climatic conditions. The consistency of the bitumen or asphalt varies also in the different courses of the same road. A lower penetration material is frequently used in the surface or wearing coat than in the lower or base course.

VISCOSITY

With viscosity the case is not so easy. Colloidal substances in cooling become viscous and, in the case of bitumen and pitch, will not pass direct from a fluid to a solid state, but over a considerable temperature range exhibit some of the properties of fluids and some of the properties of solids, and may be described as plastic solids. Bitumen or asphalt can easily be broken, yet, if it is allowed to remain in one place long enough, its equilibrium will be found to be unstable. It will flow even under the slight inequality due to its own weight. "Viscosity" must, therefore, be regarded as an important feature, being due to internal friction, a force which for ever tends to prevent the movement of the layers over each other. To appreciate this it is necessary to visualize a liquid, and tars and the more fluid bitumens may be so regarded, as being composed of the thinnest possible layers superimposed on each other. With this mental picture it is not difficult to grasp the principle which underlies the testing for viscosity. For further information on the subjects of specific gravity, penetration, and viscosity the reader is referred to Volume 2 of the Roadmakers' Library (Edward Arnold & Co.) which deals with *The Testing of Bituminous Mixtures*.

ELASTICITY

Sometimes, owing to carelessness of thought, resiliency and elasticity are regarded as one and the same thing, but they are not. The elasticity of a body means its property, when subjected to force, to change its bulk or shape and to retain it in such changed conditions until the force is removed, when it resumes its former condition and remains at rest in the bulk and shape peculiar to it before the application of the external force. Any body which requires force to keep it in a particular bulk and shape may be considered to possess elasticity. A body possessing any degree of elasticity of shape is a solid. A fluid has no elasticity of shape but possesses elasticity of bulk to perfection. Resiliency, on the other hand, is the capacity of an elastic body under strain to give back a certain quantity of work before returning to its previous condition of rest or freedom from stress. The resiliency of any body should be regarded as the extreme limit to which it can repeatedly be strained without fracture or permanent change of shape. Experiments have proved that, when force is reckoned in gravitation measure, resistance per unit of the spring's mass is simply the height that the spring itself, or an equal weight, could be lifted against gravity by an amount of work equal to that given back by the spring returning from the stressed condition. This enables the term springiness or resiliency of a load to be understood. The elasticity and resilience of an ordinary water-bound road are the measure of the capacity of the binding motive to retain moisture. The stones forming such a road are held together, like a mosaic paving, partly by friction but to a considerable extent by the elastic tension of the wet slurry with which such road was compacted at the time of rolling. The moment this becomes dry the stones and earthy matter, which possess in themselves insufficient elasticity or resiliency, are unable to react to the stresses and strains set up by vehicular traffic, and become disintegrated.

The continued stretching, bending, and varying stresses,

in any road may cause fatigue in the bitumen or tar and produce a physical change, and in no way, apart from weathering, for the purpose of this argument, associated with chemical changes. It is this capacity for resistance to stresses and strains and for retaining waterproof properties and general resistance to change over long periods, that makes bitumen such a valuable material in road surfacing.

CHAPTER XV

COATED MACADAM—TAR AND BITUMEN

THE opening years of the present century marked a distinct advance over the old methods of water-bound macadam system of road surfacing. The pioneers had discovered, though many years earlier, the high value possessed by tar for holding together the pieces of stone, instead of the earthy matter which depended entirely upon its water content to ensure adhesion.

Tar is derived from the destructive distillation of bituminous coal in the retorts and coke ovens of gas works. The coal is heated out of contact with air in vertical, inclined or horizontal retorts. This operation breaks down the compounds, and yields coke, gases, ammoniacal liquors, and oily distillates known as tars or hydrocarbons. The complexities of this process are such that the specially trained chemist is the only person who can theorize with sufficient knowledge on this subject. Tar contains carbon, hydrogen, nitrogen, sulphur, and oxygen, of which 75 per cent is the first named element, but all tars vary in percentages and compounds, owing to the different qualities of coal from which they are distilled and the method of distillation.

TAR FOR ROADS

For road making purposes, refined or distilled tar is used, and not crude tar, because the last-named would be deficient in body and viscosity, and would run and not be heavy enough when compounded with stone aggregates to adhere to them. The crude tar is first dehydrated and then goes through a process of fractional distillation which is continued until the tar is of the required viscosity or consistency. There was a growing tendency to employ higher viscosity tars in the manufacture of tar macadam, the benefits of which were reflected in the improved binding quality and stability of the material.

Road makers were greatly aided in their work by the specifications of the British Standards Institution for tars, which indicated the important elements and conditions for success. All the other elements, such as gas liquor and the ammoniacal compounds, are useless for road making purposes owing to their unstable and non-cementitious character.

VISCOSITY

Viscosity is the factor which is most difficult to provide for, as it alters with the temperature, and must vary with the character of the aggregates employed and the period which has to elapse between the manufacture of the tar macadam and its use in position on the road.

The following is an excerpt from the Foreword of B.S. 76 : 1943 (*Tars for Road Purposes*), on this subject of viscosity: "To meet all requirements, the viscosity range covered by the old specifications has been expanded in both directions, and this wide range makes it impossible to record all viscosities at a single test temperature. To avoid the confusion that might arise from the use of various test temperatures, a new system of indicating viscosity has been introduced, namely, the Equi-Viscous Temperature or E.V.T. This is the temperature in °C. at which the tar has a time of flow of 50 seconds measured by the standard tar viscometer. Its use enables the viscosity of any road tar, whether very fluid or very viscous, to be expressed on a single scale. The value becomes progressively higher as the viscosity increases."

An appendix furnishes a simple method of converting to E.V.T. the time of flow in seconds at a number of test temperatures.

DENSITY AND SPECIFIC GRAVITY

The following is an excerpt from *Standard Methods for Testing Tar and Its Products*, Second Edition, 1938—

"In the 1929 edition of 'Standard Methods,' the Committee recorded its view that density (mass per unit volume), being a fundamental concept, was to be preferred to specific gravity (the ratio of the density of a substance to the density of water, the temperature of the substance and of the water being specified). The Committee's investigations at that time showed, however, that, while the employment of density instead of specific gravity was increasing both in scientific and industrial work, the established custom in the tar and tar products trade was to use specific gravity as the basis of specifications and the measurement of liquids in bulk. Consequently, specific gravity tests alone appeared in the 1929 edition of 'Standard Methods.'

"The relative merits of working on a density basis and on a specific gravity basis have since that time been admirably discussed from a detached standpoint, and with special attention to the use of one or the other in specifications and in the measurement of liquids in bulk, notably in a paper 'Hydrometers and Hydrometry,' appearing in the *Report of the World Petroleum Congress*, vol. ii, page 880, London, 1933; and in B.S. 718 : 1936—*Density Hydrometers*, Appendix E of which is largely devoted to this particular point.

"The question of standardizing on the basis of density or specific gravity has again been closely examined by the Committee, which decided that, as its function is to issue standard methods for the tests required for tar and tar products provision must be made in the present edition for both density and specific gravity determinations."

The British Standards Institution, incorporated by Royal Charter, formerly the British Engineering Standards Association, which was formed in 1901 as the Engineering Standards Committee, has issued several Standard Specifications for the various types of coated macadam.

Tar and bitumen together or separately are used in the manufacture of coated macadam. With bitumen it is possible to use a softer tar, and the product yields a matrix with sufficient body with a reduced danger of brittleness. Bitumen, when used with tar, adds to its recuperative properties, and eliminates the tendency to "bleeding" or globular formation during hot weather. Tar, however, has been so much improved for road work that the admixture of bitumen is not, nowadays, as essential as formerly for all types of tars.

British Standards Institution's Specification for Tar Macadam, No. 802 : 1938, sets out in detail with what conditions the aggregate and filler (when filler is used) should comply, and how the grading should be specified. It also gives the quantity of binder required, in gallons per ton, for the ordinary and semi-hot and hot process; and sets out, in table form, the temperatures of mixing. The method of mixing is also fully described.

In 1945 the Institution issued Specification 802 under the title *British Standard for Tar Macadam and Tar Carpets—Granite, Limestone, and Slag Aggregates*, and in the Foreword it is noted that important developments have been made in the preparation and use of tarred materials, and that the range of road tars had been increased. In consequence of this a revision of the Standard for tar macadam had been undertaken in which not only had the clauses of the previous Specification been modified but the more recently developed types of surfacing materials had been included. The revised Specification states how the tar-macadam shall be delivered from the plant to the site of the work. In this connexion it is to be noted that the preparation of coated macadam in bulk by manufacturers has become, and rightly so, very popular, as the production of this material needs the constant attention of both the chemical and mechanical experts, which can only be demanded, as a reasonable economic proposition, in those places where the output is large.

When coated macadam has to be sent by rail, it is necessary to make it at such an initial consistency or viscosity that it will remain sufficiently plastic for handling and spreading at the site of the road work. It must not be too mobile during hot weather, so as to cause a loss of matrix in transit, or become too hard and set during cold seasons as to make removal from trucks a difficult and expensive operation. When the materials are prepared at site of work, and can be laid hot, the viscosity test ceases to be so important, and the penetration test has to be applied. In the preparation of the matrix, fine powders or fillers may be used, such as cement or fine stone dust, the action of which is colloidal, to increase the surface energy of the tar and bitumen.

The aggregates and fillers used in the manufacture of coated macadam vary with localities, but any stone that has been proved to be suitable for making a water bound road can be used; whilst slag, if properly selected, has been proved by long practice to be an ideal material owing to its capacity for holding tar, due to its high porosity. A hard crystalline limestone is eminently suitable, but, as lime has an immediate hardening effect, the viscosity of the tar should be rather less than in the case of a granite, basalt, or whinstone. Some sandstones and limestones, owing to softness, may break up under a heavy roller, but when this kind of aggregate is used its absorbent character minimizes the tendency to " bleed," or for the tar to form globules at the road surface, during periods of high temperature. When slag is used variations in quality may lead to failure, as hard pieces, when mixed with softer ones, may cause unequal wear and the formation of holes.

Coated macadam made with tar for road surfacings is specified in British Standard 802: 1945, *Tar Macadam and Tar Carpets with Granite, Limestone, or Slag Aggregate.* The specification sets out in detail with what conditions the aggregate and filler (when filler is used) should comply, and how the gradings of the different base courses and wearing courses should be specified. It also gives the type and quantity of binder required for the ordinary semi-hot and hot process and sets out, in table form, the temperatures of mixing. The methods of mixing and delivery to the site are also fully described.

In this connexion, it is to be noted that the preparation of coated macadam in large fixed plants usually situated in quarries or slag works has become the general practice, as the production of the material needs careful supervision and chemical control which can only be provided as a reasonable economic proposition in those places where the output is large. Tar macadam for footpaths is specified in B.S. 1242.

In 1950 a new Standard B.S. 1621, *Bitumen Macadam with Crushed Rock or Slag Aggregate*, was issued in view of the extensive use of bitumen in road surfacings. A further Standard B.S. 1690: 1950, *Fine Cold Asphalt*, covers the production of a durable fine-grained carpet which can be laid as a wearing course or stored for use as patching material.

The output and use of these materials has continued to grow, since the introduction of mechanical laying machines. Each machine is capable of dealing with about six times the quantity of coated macadam laid by a normal road gang, and with the minimum of inconvenience to road users. These machines enable a uniform non-skid surfacing to be produced.

POST-WAR ROADS

The coated macadam industry, by practical developments, has done much to make it possible for our roads to have their surfaces renewed without necessitating complete reconstruction, thus enabling them to carry the ever-increasing traffic.

CHAPTER XVI

BITUMEN AND ASPHALT

BEFORE considering the important topics connected with the actual mixtures as laid on the road in the form of rock asphalt (compressed asphalt), mastic asphalt, rolled asphalt, or other forms of asphalt paving, it is essential to discuss the nomenclature of this class of materials. There has in the past been considerable confusion concerning nomenclature, and even to-day many of the terms are employed in a very wide sense. For example, asphalt and bitumen are frequently regarded as one and the same, whilst tars are often included in the same category. For a proper understanding of the whole subject of bituminous road making, however, it is essential that a clear differentiation be made between these and other materials concerned.

Much of the old confusion of terms has been eliminated by the adoption of an official set of definitions recognized by all the important countries of the world with, unfortunately, the exception of the United States of America. The principal definitions from this list are as follows:

Bitumens. Mixtures of hydrocarbons of natural or pyrogeneous origin or combinations of both (frequently accompanied by their non-metallic derivatives) which can be gaseous, liquid, semi-solid or solid and which are completely soluble in carbon disulphide.

Asphaltic Bitumen. Natural or naturally occurring bitumen, or bitumen prepared from natural hydrocarbons or from derivatives of natural hydrocarbons by distillation or oxidation or cracking; solid or viscous, containing a low percentage of volatile products; possessing characteristic agglomerating properties, and substantially soluble in carbon disulphide.

Asphalt. Natural or mechanical mixtures in which the asphaltic bitumen is associated with inert mineral matter.

The word "asphalt" is to be qualified by one indicating the origin of the product.

Black to dark brown solid or semi-solid materials which gradually liquefy when heated in which the predominating constituents are bitumens, all of which occur in the solid or semi-solid form in nature or are obtained by refining petroleums or which are combinations of the bitumens mentioned with each other or with petroleums or derivatives thereof.

Lake Asphalt. A naturally occurring intimate association primarily of asphaltic bitumen and finely divided mineral matter from Trinidad or Bermudez, etc.

Natural Asphalt. Mixtures occurring in nature, in which asphaltic bitumen is associated with inert mineral matter.

Asphaltic Cement. Asphaltic bitumen or a mixture therewith prepared for use as a binder for a mineral aggregate.

A fluxed or unfluxed asphalt specially prepared as to quality and consistency for direct use in the manufacture of bituminous pavements, and having a penetration at 25° C. (77° F.) of between 5 and 250, under a load of 100 grams applied for 5 seconds (A.S.T.M. Standards).

Tar. A bituminous product, viscous or resulting from the destructive distillation of carbonaceous materials.

The word "tar" must always be preceded by the name of the matter from which it is produced: coal, shale, peat, vegetable matter, etc. Its mode of production should also be indicated.

Black to dark brown bituminous condensates, which yield substantial quantities of pitch when partially evaporated or fractionally distilled and which are produced by destructive distillation of organic material, such as coal, oil, lignite, peat and wood.

The commercial use of bitumen is as old as civilization. This is, perhaps, a rather startling statement, but is nevertheless true, as brick-work dating from about 3200 B.C., with asphalt as a mortar for pointing purposes has been found in Mesopotamia. Although it has not been definitely proved, the use of asphalt in the Indus valley probably started at an even earlier period; whilst extensive road work employing bitumen in conjunction with paving-bricks has been found in Babylon dating from the days of King Nebuchadnezzar.

With the rise and fall of the Roman Empire the use of bitumen seems to have diminished and was almost forgotten for centuries. The commercial use of bitumen in the modern sense of the word may be said to date from the discovery of rock asphalt deposits in Switzerland and Germany in the first half of the eighteenth century, although it was not until the nineteenth century that bitumen was used for road work in England.

The sources from which bitumen for road work are drawn may be divided into three groups—

1. Natural deposits in which the bitumen is found in a more or less pure state, or associated with a limited proportion of mineral matter.

2. Natural deposits which consist essentially of rocks *impregnated* with bitumen.

3. The residues from the distillation of specially chosen crude petroleum.

The principal material falling under the first category is Trinidad Lake asphalt—a hard black substance "quarried" from the asphalt lake in the West Indies. This is passed through a refinery on the lakeside in order to remove water and vegetable matter after which it is exported to all parts of the world under the name of Epuré. This material is amazingly constant in composition and an analysis of

any sample taken from batches received in any part of
the world at any time will be found to be as follows—

Bitumen soluble in CS_2	$53 \cdot 0$–$55 \cdot 0\%$
Mineral matter	$36 \cdot 0$–$37 \cdot 0\%$
Organic insoluble	$9 \cdot 0$–$10 \cdot 0\%$
Specific gravity at $15°$ C. . . .	$1 \cdot 40$
Penetration (I.P.T.) at $25°$ C. . .	$1 \cdot 5$–$4 \cdot 0$
Softening point (R. & B.) . . .	$94°$ C.–$97°$ C.
Fixed carbon	$10 \cdot 8$–$12 \cdot 0\%$
Sulphur	$6 \cdot 0$–$8 \cdot 0\%$

In this form it is too hard for direct use and is softened
or fluxed by admixture with a semi-solid or fluid petroleum
residue prior to incorporation into an asphalt mixture.

The bitumen-impregnated rocks of class (2), as above,
are usually referred to as natural asphalt rocks or natural
rock asphalts. There are deposits of this class of material
in many parts, the principal sources of supply so far as this
country is concerned being the Departments of Gard
and Ain in France; the Val de Travers in Switzerland;
Sicily, and the Hanover district of Germany. In all these
cases the rock is a limestone impregnated with bitumen
up to 11 per cent. The material is quarried or mined in
the ordinary way and is normally exported in lump form,
to be ground in this country at factories, designed for the
purpose, where it is enriched by the addition of bitumen.

The last main source of bitumen—the distillation of
crude petroleum—provides the products necessary to flux
the hard natural materials, and for the manufacture of
asphaltic mixtures for single- and two-coat work; for
jointing purposes; and for surface dressing. The majority
of these "asphaltic bitumens," as they are termed, are prepared at refineries in this country from petroleum imported
from such oil fields as Trinidad, Mexico, Venezuela, Texas,
and others. The principal characteristics of a typical
bitumen of this class are as follows—

Bitumen soluble in CS_2	$99 \cdot 5\%$
Mineral matter	Trace
Organic insoluble	Nil
Specific gravity at $15°$ C. . . .	$1 \cdot 03$
Penetration (I.P.T.) at $25°$ C. . .	65
Softening point (R. & B.) . . .	$55°$ C.

B.S. 594 : 1950 states that the asphaltic cement, as selected by the engineer, shall comply with the requirements given in the following table—

PROPERTIES OF ASPHALTIC CEMENT
(For mixtures for general application)

Property	Asphaltic Cement					
	1		2		3	
	Asphaltic Bitumen		Refined Lake Asphalt (Fluxed)		Equal Proportions of Asphaltic Bitumen of appropriate penetration and Refined Lake Asphalt	
	Min.	Max.	Min.	Max.	Min.	Max.
Penetration at 25° C. (77° F.)	40	60	40	60	40	60
Softening point °C. (R. and B.) (°F.)	50 (122)	60 (140)	50 (122)	60 (140)	50 (122)	60 (140)
Ductility at 25° C. (77° F.)	50	—	30	—	50	—
Solubility in carbon disulphide (per cent)	99·5	—	60	70	75	79
Ash (per cent)	—	0·5	26	32	17	19
Flash point °C. (open) (°F.)	175 (347)	—	175 (347)	—	175 (347)	—
Specific gravity at 15·5° C./15·5° C. (60° F./60° F.)	1·00	1·06	1·20	1·34	1·17	1·20
Loss on heating for 5 hours at 163°C. (325°F.) (per cent)	—	2·0	—	2·0	—	2·0
Penetration of residue (percentage of original)	60	—	60	—	60	—

NOTE 1. The tests for the above properties shall be carried out in accordance with the methods set out in the current edition of *Standard Methods of Testing Petroleum and its Products* published by the Institute of Petroleum.

NOTE 2. In special circumstances, and by agreement between the engineer and the contractor, a harder grade of bitumen (e.g. 30/40 penetration) may be used.

PROPERTIES OF ASPHALTIC CEMENT

(For base-course and wearing-course mixtures in situations where high rainfall and/or colder conditions prevail)

Property	Asphaltic Cement					
	1		2		3	
	Asphaltic Bitumen		Refined Lake Asphalt (Fluxed)		Equal Proportions of Asphaltic Bitumen of appropriate penetration and Refined Lake Asphalt	
	Min.	Max.	Min.	Max.	Min.	Max.
Penetration at 25° C. (77° F.)	60	80	60	80	60	80
Softening point °C. (R. and B.) (°F.)	45 (113)	55 (131)	45 (113)	55 (131)	45 (113)	55 (131)
Ductility at 25° C. (77° F.)	50	—	30	—	50	—
Solubility in carbon disulphide (per cent)	99·5	—	60	70	75	79
Ash (per cent)	—	0·5	26	32	17	19
Flash point °C. (open) (°F.)	175 (347)	—	175 (347)	—	175 (347)	—
Specific gravity at 15·5° C./15·5° C. (60° F./60° F.)	1·00	1·06	1·20	1·34	1·17	1·20
Loss on heating for 5 hours at 163°C. (325°F.) (per cent)	—	2·0	—	2·0	—	2·0
Penetration of residue (percentage of original)	60	—	60	—	60	—

NOTE. The tests for the above properties shall be carried out in accordance with the methods set out in the current edition of *Standard Methods of Testing Petroleum and its Products* published by the Institute of Petroleum.

ADVANTAGES

The advantages of asphalt roads may be summarized as follows—

They are durable. Many major roads and streets with asphalt surfaces have carried the heaviest traffic for twenty years or more.

They are economical. Proof of this is patent if the first cost of any road is divided by the number of years of its estimated life.

They are noiseless. The reduction in the amount of vibration, by the absorption of shock in an asphalt road, can only be fully appreciated after actual experience.

They are sanitary. Having an impervious surface and being free from joints or cracks, no crevices occur in which dust can accumulate, germs develop, or offensive odours arise from decomposing matter.

They are easily repaired. Ordinary wear and tear has little effect on a properly constructed asphalt road; and a patch can be made with so much neatness that it is soon impossible to distinguish it from the original work.

They require the minimum of tractive effort. An important economic factor, which means a saving in the cost of running and maintaining road vehicles.

Colour. Normal asphalt surfaces provide under wear a not unpleasing grey appearance. With the modern technique of utilizing light-coloured aggregates and pigments, attractive and restful effects can be obtained.

THIN APPLICATION MIXTURES

In the opening paragraph of Chapter X it was noted that the water-bound macadam roads received a new lease of life by the application of surface dressings. This kind of work, which is generally carried out in the spring and early summer, is an annually recurring charge, and although its utility is beyond calculation, it does in some places lead to temporary annoyance.

Before the Roads Department of the Ministry of Transport made experiments with what is termed "Thin Application Mixtures," such mixtures had already been developed by the Industry. These mixtures, which will need no annual surface dressing, and in the construction of which asphalt, bitumen, tar, tar and bitumen, or emulsions may be employed, are laid and consolidated after the old road surfaces have been scarified and properly shaped. This system is also being successfully and economically applied to old and worn bituminous road surfaces, in which cases the surface is first burnt off to the required depth. In all these up-to-date methods of road construction, economy is an important factor, therefore road-makers are hoping to reduce the heavy cost of annual dressing by the substitution of a surface which, after laying, will remain in a non-skid condition throughout its life.

CHAPTER XVII

ROLLED ASPHALT PAVING

In contradistinction to tar macadam, which may contain a varying percentage of bitumen, the matrix of asphalt pavements should be of bitumen and/or asphalt only, and this ought to be regarded as the distinguishing characteristic, and a most important one, of the two classes of work. The former ought to be styled as tar macadam, whether it contains bitumen or not, and the latter as a bituminous or asphalt macadam. But there is a most perplexing vagueness about the terms in common use, and it is very difficult to know how to draw the lines of demarcation between the various methods of construction in which bitumen and tar play such important parts.

For bituminous surface work, a suitable foundation is as essential as it is for every other class of road construction. A well-known road maker, who has had considerable experience in this method of road construction, has stated that the shock absorbing quality of a bituminous wearing coat when laid on a hardcore foundation of destructor clinker, is greater than when laid on a concrete foundation, and that this method of construction reduces the tendency to corrugations. Whatever materials may be used in the formation of the foundation for a bituminous surface coat, whether Portland cement concrete, "hardcore" (destructor clinker, bricks or stone) or asphalt concrete, a bed of 3 to 6 inches of lightly consolidated ashes should be laid on the subsoil to act as an insulating layer. When the foundation coat has been sufficiently made, its surface, whilst retaining a roughness to form a key to receive what is termed a "binder course," should be at correct approximate levels.

BASE COURSE

This base course, which should have a consolidated

thickness of $1\frac{1}{2}$ to 3 inches, can be made of any suitable local stone, or clinker. It forms, as its name indicates, a binder between the wearing or surface coat and the foundation, and such a method of construction ensures the maximum amount of resiliency, which is an important factor in successful road construction, and for the easy and economical running of all types of vehicles. This method of construction causes the forces of pressure, due both to dead loads and impact, to be distributed over a large area of foundation and, in this way, resists the mechanical agencies which would otherwise tend to the deformation of the wearing coat. In other words, it acts as a cushion for the reduction of impact shocks, which are finally absorbed by the foundation. It is not improbable that in the development of this, and other similar types of construction, the foundation may be designed to consist of broken stone aggregate and an asphaltic cement. On a rigid road the forces of reaction would remit some of these shocks to the creating agent—the vehicle. It is in this respect that the value of the asphalt or bituminous road, is best realized.

The quantities of materials for the base course must vary with local conditions. The largest size of stone should not be more than one-half and not less than one-third of the final thickness of the consolidated course; the proportion of stone of this size shall be not less than 40 per cent of the total stone content. The composition of base-course mixtures should conform with the following table.

PERCENTAGE OF WEIGHT

Stone	Soluble Bitumen		Aggregate Passing $\frac{3}{16}$ in. Mesh B.S. Sieve	
	Min.	Max.	Min.	Max.
55	6·0	7·0	38·0	39·0
60	5·6	6·6	34·4	34·4
65	5·2	6·2	28·8	29·8
70	4·9	5·9	24·1	25·1
75	4·5	5·5	19·5	20·5

The matrix (asphaltic cement) will also vary with the source of supply, and may be modified to meet the requirements of the foundation and for local conditions. Generally speaking, however, a penetration of from 40–70 is employed in both base course and wearing surface mixtures, although these figures may be varied under special circumstances from 30–100. Local conditions together with the type of asphaltic cement (i.e. natural asphalt or asphaltic bitumen) have a bearing on this. For heavily trafficked roads there can be no doubt as to the value of this two-coat method of road construction, which possesses the great advantage of having a wearing coat superimposed on what is really an asphalt concrete foundation.

For two-coat work, the surface or wearing coat may be from 1 to 1½ inches in thickness; and one ton of prepared materials should cover from 14 to 20 yards super. The approximate grading of the sand should be as follows—

	Percentage of Weight	
	Min.	Max.
Passing a No. 200 mesh	0	3
Passing a No. 72 mesh retained on a No. 200 mesh	15	55
Passing a No. 25 mesh retained on a No. 72 mesh	25	70
Passing a No. 7 mesh retained on a No. 25 mesh	2	25
Retained on a No. 7 mesh	0	5

The sand used in this class of work determines not only the maximum density of the finished surface, and homogeneity is essential to success, but its fineness and freedom from clay or organic matter enable it to act as a vehicle for the complete utilization of all bitumen; free bitumen is a source of weakness in the road structure.

COMPOSITION OF WEARING-COURSE MIXTURES

Schedule number	Type of surfacing		Percentage by weight					
		Stone	Soluble bitumen		Aggregate passing 200 mesh B.S. sieve		Aggregate retained on 200 mesh B.S. sieve but passing 7 mesh B.S. sieve	
			Min.	Max.	Min.	Max.	Min.	Max.
5	Sand-carpet	0	9·8	10·8	12·0	14·0	75·2	78·2
	Sand and stone	15	8·6	9·6	10·0	12·0	63·4	66·4
		20	8·2	9·2	9·3	11·3	59·5	62·5
		25	7·8	8·8	8·6	10·6	55·6	58·6
6	Sand-carpet	0	10·8	11·8	14·0	16·0	72·2	75·2
	Sand and stone	15	9·6	10·6	12·0	14·0	60·4	63·4
		20	9·2	10·2	11·3	13·3	56·5	59·5
		25	8·8	9·8	10·6	12·5	52·7	55·6
7*	Sand-carpet	0	11·8	12·8	16·0	18·0	69·2	72·2
	Sand and stone	15	10·6	11·5	14·0	16·0	57·5	60·4
		20	10·2	11·1	13·3	15·3	53·6	56·5
		25	9·8	10·7	12·5	14·5	49·8	52·7

NOTE. The composition of asphalt best suited to local traffic and climate will vary with the conditions at the site. The selection of the correct schedule and appropriate mixture should therefore be made by reference to the notes on composition of mixtures in Appendix A.

* Schedule 7 relates to rich mixtures which are recommended only for specific circumstances, e.g. where high rainfall and/or colder conditions prevail.

SINGLE COURSE

A single-course bituminous surface gives most excellent results, even for heavy traffic, and is an economical method of construction, as it can be laid direct on to an existing surface. For this class of work both the coarse and fine

COMPOSITION OF SINGLE-COURSE MIXTURES

Schedule number	Stone content	Soluble bitumen		Aggregate passing 200 mesh B.S. sieve		Aggregate retained on 200 mesh B.S. sieve but passing 7 mesh B.S. sieve	
		Min.	Max.	Min.	Max.	Min.	Max.
1	25	7·8	8·8	8·6	10·6	55·6	58·6
	30	7·4	8·4	7·9	9·9	51·7	54·7
	35	7·0	8·0	7·2	9·1	47·9	50·8
	40	6·6	7·6	6·4	8·4	44·0	47·0
	45	6·2	7·2	5·8	7·8	40·0	43·0
	50	5·8	6·8	5·1	7·1	36·1	39·1
	55	5·4	6·3	4·4	6·4	32·3	35·2
	60	5·0	5·9	3·7	5·7	28·4	31·3
2	25	8·8	9·8	10·6	12·5	52·7	55·6
	30	8·4	9·4	9·9	11·8	48·8	51·7
	35	8·0	9·0	9·1	11·1	44·9	47·9
	40	7·6	8·5	8·4	10·4	41·1	44·0
	45	7·2	8·1	7·8	9·8	37·1	40·0
	50	6·8	7·7	7·1	9·1	33·2	36·1
	55	6·3	7·2	6·4	8·4	29·4	32·3
	60	5·9	6·8	5·7	7·7	25·5	28·4
3*	25	9·8	10·7	12·5	14·5	49·8	52·7
	30	9·4	10·3	11·8	13·8	45·9	48·8
	35	9·0	9·9	11·1	13·1	42·0	44·9
	40	8·5	9·4	10·4	12·4	38·2	41·1
	45	8·1	9·0	9·8	11·8	34·2	37·1
	50	7·7	8·6	9·1	11·1	30·3	33·2
	55	7·2	8·1	8·4	10·4	26·5	29·4
	60	6·8	7·7	7·7	9·7	22·6	25·5

All percentages are by weight.

NOTE. The best composition of asphalt will vary according to the traffic and climatic conditions at the site. The selection of the correct schedule and appropriate mixture should therefore be made by reference to the notes under "Composition of Mixtures," in Appendix A.

* Schedule 3 relates to rich mixtures which are recommended only for specific circumstances, e.g. where high rainfall and/or colder conditions prevail.

SINGLE COAT ASPHALT SURFACE ON OLD WATER BOUND ROAD—SUNKEN KERBS

Compare with Plate on page 90, as it is the same section of road

(*Photo: Tecart Studios, London, W.C.1*)

aggregates must be carefully graded, to combine all the materials which are employed when two courses are laid.

The finished thickness of the materials in this one-course work should be not less than $1\frac{1}{2}$ inches.

With an asphaltic bitumen the quantities will be somewhat different from the above, as no finely divided mineral matter is present in the asphaltic cement as in the case of a fluxed lake asphalt.

In the manufacture of single coat asphalt mixtures the aggregates are heated to a temperature of 300–375° F. The asphaltic cement is added at a temperature not exceeding 375° F., and the whole properly incorporated in mechanical mixers. In about 2 minutes the mixing operation is finished. The same temperatures and procedure obtain for the mixing of binder and wearing surface mixtures. The materials should be at the site of the road work as soon as possible after mixing, and the temperature of the mass should never be less than 250° F. at the time of spreading. This means that the effective radius of operations from a central plant is about 40 miles when suitable motor vehicles are employed for conveying the prepared materials. On arrival at the site of the road work, the asphalt is tipped from the transporting vehicle, and spread to the required thickness and contour. As soon as the heat approximates that of the air temperature, generally about 6 hours after rolling, though varying with climatic conditions, traffic can be passed over the new road surface. It will thus be noted that the expeditious manner in which this kind of work can be done, gives it a rightful claim to that popularity which has been gained in recent years under the demand of modern high speed heavy traffic. For rolling this class of material 6- to 9-ton rollers should be employed.

OLD ROADS AS FOUNDATION

Many of the old roads of this country have become so compacted by traffic that the crust forms a good foundation; consequently, in all such cases where the levels permit, an economical and satisfactory paving can be obtained by laying single coat materials on the old surface. The success of this method of road surfacing depends on the proper grading of the aggregates, as inaccurate grading or the use of an unsuitable matrix, either physically unsuitable or of wrong consistency, is responsible for waves or corrugations about which complaints were formerly often heard.

CAUSES OF FAILURE

When defects occur in this class of road construction, the cause or causes may be traced to one or more of the following reasons—

1. A weak or insufficient foundation. A sound base, either rigid or resilient, is an essential feature of the modern highway.

2. Improper bond between the base course and the wearing surface.

3. Insufficient lateral support, without which the materials may creep or disintegrate under vehicular traffic.

4. Displacement of surface, causing wave formations, due either to defects in materials, methods of mixing or to the fact that, during periods of high temperature, when laid on a concrete bed the surface may move longitudinally in the direction of the traffic. When a concrete foundation is provided the surface should be left rough, and an asphaltic cement, preferably of low penetration, employed.

5. Unless great care is exercised in raking the hot mixture to an even thickness before consolidation, initial corrugations of the surface may result.

6. Judicious rolling is necessary, and with a roller exceeding 8 tons in weight it is easy to intensify initial corrugations. If a friable or soft stone is used, the aggregate may be crushed under the weight of a heavy roller.

7. The mixture may have been applied in too thick a coat, resulting in waviness and corrugations.

In the production and use of bituminous paving it can,

with confidence, be asserted that durability, economy, rapidity of construction, easy maintenance, little frictional resistance for wheels, impervious and sanitary surface, and the minimum of slipperiness and noise, are obtained. But most important of all, as already pointed out, resiliency is secured, and when this class of material is used for road making its popularity is, in consequence, considerably enhanced, as easy running is secured on a shock absorbing surface. The comfort of the road user is obtained with the minimum and not the maximum depreciation of the vehicle employed. Freedom from vibration, either periodic or sudden, with excessive and destructive impact, is the desideratum which this type of road surface provides.

B.S. 594 : 1950 is replete with information and data on the subject of two-course rolled asphalt with gravel aggregate.

"CUTBACKS"

The use of "cutbacks," an American term, which means an asphaltic bitumen of appropriate penetration fluxed with a tar or petroleum distillate to bring it to the correct viscosity for the purpose for which it is required, has increased considerably during recent years both for surface dressing and for the coating of stone.

Until a few years ago it was the general opinion that mineral aggregates coated with asphaltic bitumen must, of necessity, be laid whilst still hot. The makers of this class of road paving material have, however, found that by the control of temperatures, both of the stone and "cutback," treated aggregate can be stored for some weeks or consigned long journeys and be readily laid at its destination. The coated stone does not need surface dressing for some years after laying, the reason being that the high melting point of the bitumen employed is not affected by ordinary atmospheric temperatures.

CHAPTER XVIII

CLINKER ASPHALT

For the development of clinker asphalt we are indebted to the determination of Mr. A. F. Holden, M.Inst.C.E., who, when he was the Engineer of the Metropolitan Borough of Fulham, realized its possibilities and importance. In these days of strict economy, too often made at the expense of road maintenance, this method of producing a reliable road material deserves the widest publicity.

Although the manufacture of clinker asphalt had very simple beginnings in the early days of the century, the position is very different to-day when a modern plant manufactures the material under almost dust-free conditions in precisely the proportions required. The clinker plant was first erected adjacent to the Fulham refuse destructor in 1924 in Townmead Road, and has since been twice modernized. Since its first erection some 50,000 tons of clinker asphalt have been produced from this plant.

The clinker used is produced by the incineration of towns' refuse in a refuse destructor under high ashpit pressure which tends to complete combustion and high cell temperatures. The clinker is discharged from the cells by hydraulic clinkering apparatus and is removed by conveyor to the crushing plant, to store or to barge for disposal.

The crushing plant, erected in 1922, comprises two vertically superposed pairs of rolls with horizontal nip, the upper pair being serrated and the lower pair plain. The clinker passes in succession through both pairs of rolls and is then transferred by a chain and bucket type elevator to a rotary screen where the respective screenings $1\frac{1}{2}$ in. to $\frac{3}{4}$ in., $\frac{3}{4}$ in. to $\frac{1}{4}$ in., $\frac{1}{4}$ in. to $\frac{1}{8}$ in., and $\frac{1}{8}$ in. down, are discharged to separate hoppers. The largest sizes screened, and the tailings, are returned for further crushing.

The capacity of the plant, which is driven by a 40 h.p.

steam engine, is about 7 tons per hour. The crushed material, which has a remarkably high coefficient of internal friction, is stored in a large shed adjoining the bituminous mixing plant ready for use. The bituminous mixing plant was erected in 1924, and reconstructed in 1939. Its capacity is about 6 tons per hour.

Crushed clinker in appropriate proportions of the various grades is delivered by a chain and bucket type elevator to the drier, which is of the rotary type, externally heated by oil fuel, fed by gravity and atomized by steam or compressed air through vertical type burners into the furnaces. The dried clinker is picked up by a similar elevator and delivered to a small storage hopper mounted over the circular measuring box which is rotated to deliver directly into the mixer. This is of the "American type" with two rotating shafts, fitted with mixing blades. The outer casing of the mixer is extended to cover the measuring box and to provide support for the storage hopper, at the same time preventing the escape of dust during the filling of the measuring box or its discharge to the mixer.

The asphaltic cement is melted in two coke-fired kettles, each of 1,000 gallons capacity, from which it is pumped to the measuring device attached to the mixer by a compressed air lifter controlled from the mixing floor. An air compressor (capacity about 80 cu. ft. of free air per minute) is provided for this purpose.

The mixed asphalt is discharged direct from the mixer to transport vehicles.

The mixing plant and its auxiliaries can be operated either by a steam engine or by a 2-phase electric motor. Steam for operation of the plant and the destructor auxiliaries is generated in three boilers heated by the flue gases from the destructor cells. Electrical energy for the same purpose is available from the public supply or alternatively from a 250 kVA 2-phase 50-cycle alternator driven by a 375 h.p. steam engine when the boiler is adequate for all requirements.

Separation of iron from the crushed clinker by the use of a small electric-magnet separator is desirable to remove nails, wire, and other small metallic articles which otherwise appear in the finished product.

MODERN MIXTURES

Clinker asphalt is manufactured with crushed and graded clinker from the Council's dust destructor plant. The matrix consists of asphaltic cement consisting of a blend of 50 per cent Trinidad Epure and 50 per cent 190/210 pen. bitumen softened to 60 penetration by the addition of a small proportion of flux. The mixed material varies slightly in composition, but an average of a large number of analyses gives the following figures—

	per cent by weight
Bitumen Soluble	16·7
Passing 200	22·8
100	5·8
85	2·5
52	2·5
36	10·2
25	5·3
18	4·0
8	6·5
1/8	8·4
3/16	5·0
1/4	4·3
3/8	5·0
1/2	1·0
	100·0 per cent

This material is frequently superimposed on a base coat mixture incorporating approximately 13 per cent by weight of soluble bitumen. It is interesting to note the comparative proportions by weight and by volume as shown on opposite page.

In addition to the extensive work carried out on a large number of heavily trafficked roads in Fulham, some work has also been carried out with a gravel/clinker base coat mixture with a normal stone-filled asphalt wearing surface.

	per cent *by weight*	*per cent* *by volume*
Fulham Borough Council Base Coat Clinker Asphalt		
Bitumen	13·0	24·8
Aggregate	87·0	75·2
Fulham Borough Council Wearing Coat Clinker Asphalt		
Bitumen	16·5	31·7
Aggregate	83·5	68·3
Normal Stone-filled Asphalt		
Bitumen	9·5	21·6
Aggregate	90·5	78·4

Amongst the special advantages accruing from the use of clinker asphalt are the following—

1. Celerity of laying and almost immediate availability for traffic.

2. Weather conditions rarely interfere with progress of the work.

3. Particularly adaptable for finishing with non-skid surfaces and for renewing same.

4. Where levels permit can be resurfaced with thin coat without disturbing old surface.

5. Does not exert side pressure on kerbs and footways.

6. Trench reinstatements and other patching can be readily and neatly performed.

7. Clean and non-absorbent surface which is readily cleansed.

8. Quiet and smooth surface for traffic.

9. Material is delivered ready for prompt laying and process tends to minimum obstruction to traffic.

10. Suitability for the surfacing of recreation grounds and park roads, etc.

11. Gives excellent service over a large number of years with little attention.

CHAPTER XIX

ROUGHENED SURFACES

THE following references to roughened surfaces and mechanical laying are taken complete from B.S. 594 : 1950 and for these and other information the author is indebted to the British Standards Institution.

ROUGHENED SURFACES

Application of Chippings. In the case of asphalt mixtures containing less than 45 per cent of stone, a roughened surface shall be obtained by the application of chippings. After initial compression, and while the asphalt is still warm and in a plastic condition, it shall be covered with a layer of $\frac{3}{4}$ inch or $\frac{1}{2}$ inch approved, clean, hard chippings. The chippings shall, prior to application, be coated with 2 per cent to 3 per cent of asphaltic cement of medium penetration (e.g. 40/50 penetration at 25° C. (77° F.)). To enable the chippings to carry the specified proportion of asphaltic cement, 2 to 3 per cent of filler shall be added either before or after the addition of the asphaltic cement.

The chippings shall be uniformly and evenly distributed at the rate of 100–160 square yards per ton (2,240 lb.) for $\frac{1}{2}$ inch chippings and 70–130 square yards per ton (2,240 lb.) for $\frac{3}{4}$ inch chippings. The chippings shall then be rolled or otherwise pressed into the surface of the asphalt.

When spreading the chippings, the channels against the kerbs shall be covered by battens, not less than 6 inches (15 cm) wide, so as to ensure that a smooth channel is maintained to facilitate the flow of surface water to the gulleys.

When the mixture contains 45 per cent, or more, of stone, chippings shall be applied only if specified by the engineer.

Joints. Care shall be taken to ensure that all joints are properly and truly made.

The transverse and longitudinal joints between the sections of work shall be cut back and painted with a thin coat of asphaltic cement so that a permanent bond is obtained, and such joints shall be accurately levelled so that the surface is uniform and true.

All manholes, kerbs, channels, and similar projections against which the mixture is to abut shall be cleaned and painted with a thin uniform coating of asphaltic cement prior to the mixture being laid. The mixture shall be tamped around and against such projections by means of hot tampers, and the finished surface shall be left flush or not exceeding $\frac{1}{8}$ inch (3·0 mm) above such projections. This requirement assumes that all necessary adjustments to the level of manhole covers, etc., are made before the asphalt is laid.

When laying channels care shall be taken to prevent the retention of surface water.

MECHANICAL LAYING

(i) *Transportation*. The mixture shall be delivered from the plant to the site of the work in vehicles previously cleaned of all foreign materials and protected, if necessary, against weather conditions. The delivery of the material shall be co-ordinated with the rate of progress of the spreading machine in order to avoid, as far as possible, interruption in spreading.

(ii) *Spreading and Finishing*. After the foundation has been swept clean, the mixture shall be laid by an approved type of mechanical spreader and finisher capable of laying to the required widths, profile, camber, or cross-fall without causing segregation, dragging, burning, or other surface defects or irregularities, and of being operated at a speed consistent with the character of the mixture and the thickness of the course being laid, so as to produce a surface having a uniform density and surface texture. The spreader shall be operated at a uniform rate and the mixture shall be fed to the spreader at such a rate as to permit continuous

laying so far as supply and site conditions permit. When
not operating on side forms, the spreader shall employ
mechanical devices such as equalizing runners, evener
arms, or other compensating devices, to adjust the grade
and confine the edges of the mixture to true lines. Before
rolling is started and immediately after any course is
placed, the surface shall be checked and all defects and
irregularities in alignment, grade, or texture corrected by
the addition or removal of mixture. The thickness of the
course shall be regulated so that, after final rolling, the
finished thickness shall be from $1\frac{1}{2}$ inches to 3 inches
(3·8 cm to 7·6 cm) as specified by the engineer. The course
shall be rolled with a roller weighing not less than 6 tons
(6,000 kg) to give a true surface which, when tested with a
straight edge 10 feet long placed parallel to the centre line
of the carriageway, shall have no depression greater than
$\frac{3}{8}$ inch, due allowance being made for the projection of
chippings in the road surface.

In the case of roads with a straight cross-fall, this fall
shall be not more than 1 in 40 and not less than 1 in 48,
unless otherwise directed by the engineer. With roads to be
cambered, the average fall of the finished surface, from the
crown to the channel, shall be not more than 1 in 30 and
not less than 1 in 45.

NOTE. The above requirements for cross-fall do not apply to
curves with super-elevation.

CHAPTER XX

COMPRESSED ASPHALT

COMPRESSED rock asphalt is not a mixture, like the other products, for making road surfaces, but is a natural asphalt powder for the construction of road wearing surfaces. Much of the asphalt rock which is used in this country for the preparation of the powder comes from France and Sicily, where extensive deposits have been exploited for a number of years. It occurs as an impregnated rock, consisting almost entirely of carboniferous limestone, of the Tertiary, Cretaceous, and Jurassic geological periods. The colour of the rock is of a deep chocolate hue. Only that of first quality, with an average 9 to 11 per cent bitumen content, is imported into this country where it is treated as described below and used for the manufacture of powder for compressed asphalt work.

The natural asphalt rock is imported in large lumps, but at the works, where the powder is manufactured, it is passed through crushers fitted with toothed rollers, and reduced in size to 2 or 3 inch pieces. These pieces are next disintegrated, and a powder is produced. When required for use the powder is heated in rotating cylinders to a temperature which must not exceed 300° F. to drive off all moisture. Experience is the dominating factor at this juncture in the manufacture of this class of material, as it is absolutely necessary to cease the roasting process at the exact moment. The powder is next loaded into motor vehicles and taken to the site of the road work and spread to the desired thickness by means of rakes. When this operation has been carried out, the powder is compressed by means of hot rammers of special form, called pelons, which cause a reduction in bulk of 40 per cent. The surface is immediately ironed by means of special heated implements to ensure water-tightness, and to prevent the surface from

LAYING COMPRESSED ASPHALT

(*Photo: Tecart Studios, London, W.C.1*)

being broken up. The finished thickness of this kind of paving is generally $1\frac{1}{2}$ to $2\frac{1}{4}$ inches.

The most striking feature of this paving is found in the fact that it continues to compress under vehicular traffic, and that wear does not commence until the maximum density has been reached.

When this type of paving is used, the foundation may be of Portland cement concrete. Asphaltic concrete may be used on an old Portland cement concrete foundation when road paving is being replaced. The Portland cement concrete must be dry when the hot powder is laid.

This class of road surface, though expensive in first cost, is the most economical paving known, owing to its long life.

It is eminently suitable for intensive town traffic, and being impervious, is sanitary, and offers the least resistance to tractive effort.

British Standards Institution's 348 : 1948 entitled *Compressed Natural Rock Asphalt* is a valuable source of information on this subject and the following is an excerpt from that publication—

TRANSPORTATION AND METHOD OF LAYING

Transportation. The powder, protected by tarpaulins or other suitable sheeting, shall be conveyed from the heaters to the roadway in wagons.

Spreading. The powder shall be spread at a temperature of about 120° C. (250° F.) and be evenly raked to such a thickness that after being compressed by ramming the finished thickness shall be from $1\frac{1}{2}$ inches to $2\frac{1}{4}$ inches (3·8 cm to 5·7 cm) as specified by the engineer.

After raking, the powder shall be compressed with heated rammers until consolidated.

Unless otherwise directed by the engineer, the fall of the finished surface from the crown of the road to the channel shall be not more than 1 in 40 and not less than 1 in 48.

NOTE. The above requirements for cross-fall do not apply in the case of curves with super-elevation.

Surface Finish. Unless otherwise specified by the engineer, the surface shall be spread with chippings in the following manner—

After initial compaction the asphalt, while still warm, shall be lightly dressed with a solution of asphaltic bitumen of approximately 200 penetration at 25° C. (77° F.) in a suitable petroleum solvent.

The surface so prepared shall be covered with a layer of approved chippings. Two-thirds of these shall be hard igneous rock 1 inch (2·5 cm) in size and one-third of a slightly less hard igneous rock ¾ inch (1·9 cm) in size, the two qualities of rock being selected so that there shall be a differential wear in service. The selection shall be approved by the engineer.

The chippings shall be coated prior to application with not less than 2 per cent nor more than 3 per cent by weight of asphaltic bitumen having a penetration at 25° C. (77° F.) not less than 100 nor greater than 300. To enable the mixture of chippings to carry the specified proportion of asphaltic bitumen, filler in the proportion of not less than 3 per cent by weight of the total mixture shall be added either before or after the addition of the asphaltic bitumen.

The chippings shall be uniformly and evenly distributed at the rate of approximately 35–40 square yards per ton (2,240 lb.), punned and subsequently rolled so as to become partially embedded in the asphalt.

The weight of the roller shall not exceed 4 tons (8,960 lb.).

When spreading and rolling the chippings, the channels against the kerbs shall be covered by battens, not less than 6 inches (15 cm.) nor more than 9 inches (23 cm.) wide, to ensure that a smooth channel is maintained to facilitate the flow of surface water to the gulleys.

Before opening to traffic, rock asphalt powder shall be lightly swept into the interstices of the consolidated surface.

Joints. Care shall be taken to ensure that all joints are properly and truly made.

The transverse and longitudinal joints between the sections of work shall be cut back, and painted with a thin coat of asphaltic cement so that a permanent mechanical bond is obtained, and such joints shall be accurately levelled so that the surface is uniform and true.

The edges of all manholes, kerbs, channels, and similar projections against which the mixture is to abut shall be cleaned and painted with a thin uniform coating of asphaltic cement prior to the mixture being laid. The mixture shall be tamped around and against such projections by means of hot tampers, and the finished surface shall be left flush or not exceeding $\frac{1}{4}$ inch (6·5 mm.) above such projections.

Care shall be taken in laying channels to prevent the retention of surface water.

CHAPTER XXI

MASTIC ASPHALT

SUCCESS followed the introduction of the carpeting process for preparing the wearing surfaces of the highways of this kingdom with mastic asphalt, in all cases where science was untrammelled either by economic interest or the inexperience of the operators.

Slipperiness was a charge that, in the past, was levelled against mastic asphalt paving. The cause of this was not far to seek and was due to the inherent properties of the bitumen with which some of the paving materials had been compounded. At times, and under certain peculiar climatic conditions, some roads did become more or less slippery, and this was responsible for the criticism which followed the adoption of this system of paving road surfaces. But, with the knowledge that has been gained by the use of pre-coated chippings, there should be no necessity for this defect to occur in future work. The reader is referred to British Standards Specification No. 1447.

WHAT IS MASTIC ASPHALT?

All types of mastic asphalt have two main components : the asphaltic cement, or cementing agent, and the aggregate. The combination of an aggregate, having a certain degree of fineness, and an asphalt cement in proper proportions produces a mastic asphalt. When melted, the mastic, as its name implies, should be fluid, but of a stability that will permit it to be worked without difficulty. If it is too fluid, or has too high a bitumen content, it will be difficult to manipulate, and the paving will not be successful. On the other hand, should the material be lacking in bitumen, any endeavour to reduce it to the correct consistency by the application of extra heat may easily result in burning. Should this happen, efficiency is at once impaired. In any case, a mastic having too low a bitumen content will be unstable and of poor weather and traffic resisting properties.

Three types of aggregate can be employed in mastic asphalt manufacture, viz.: rock asphalts, hard limestones, and siliceous limestones. In considering the use of rock asphalt, it is necessary to state that Nature has impregnated these rocks with bitumen, and that, whatever function the bitumen may perform, it acts as a vehicle for any further matrix which may be added during manufacture, producing, with proper care, an efficient and homogeneous product.

ROCK ASPHALTS

Of the rock asphalts the most important commercial deposits are those of Sicily, St. Jean de Maurejol in France, the Neuchâtel-Val-de-Travers region of Switzerland and the Vorwohle deposits of Germany. From a purely physical point of view, these rocks vary considerably, and it is these varied physical characteristics which make the difference in the finished product; and each requires different treatment. In a sample of rock asphalt of good quality, the bitumen must be evenly impregnated throughout the mass. An unevenly impregnated rock may be due to the fact that a limestone of an absorbent nature is present in small fissures only, and that the bitumen has travelled along these, and has left the remainder, possibly a hard crystalline limestone, incapable of impregnation.

In manufacturing paving mastic from rock asphalt the selected rock is ground to a relatively coarse powder. Reference to British Standards Institution Specification No. 596 shows that this is fixed at a minimum of 15 per cent passing a 200 mesh sieve, the remainder graded to pass an 8 mesh sieve.

The reason for grinding the rock to powder before incorporating it with bitumen will be obvious. It is not necessary, however, to observe too close limits on this grinding process since the rock asphalt has a natural grading which it assumes during manufacture and which has little bearing on the initial grinding it receives.

The preliminary crushing process is dependent on the class of rock asphalt employed and such details call for wide experience and careful control.

The relation between the rock asphalt as ground and its natural grading in the finished mastic is illustrated by the following typical figures—

(1) *Grading of rock asphalt powder before manufacture—*

		Per cent
Passing 200 mesh B.S. mesh sieve	. .	22
,, 72 ,, and retained on 200 mesh sieve	.	32
,, 25 ,, and retained on 85 mesh sieve	.	25
,, 7 ,, and retained on 36 mesh sieve	.	21

(2) *Grading of aggregate recovered from analysis of final mixture—*

		Per cent
Passing 200 mesh B.S. mesh sieve	. .	48
,, 72 ,, and retained on 200 mesh sieve	.	17
,, 25 ,, . and retained on 85 mesh sieve	.	19
,, 7 ,, and retained on 36 mesh sieve	.	16

The change in grading is brought about with the incorporation of the rock asphalt powder with the added bitumen during the process of manufacture, and is due to the influence of heat and the shearing action of the mixing.

LIMESTONE

Reference was made in a previous paragraph to the use of limestone and siliceous limestone as the aggregate for mastic paving manufacture.

Materials based on these aggregates are often graphically though erroneously termed synthetic mastic. Their use has arisen from the attempt to produce mastic which has general characteristics similar to the original rock asphalt mastic but with cheaper aggregates.

The relative merits of the two types have been the subject of considerable controversy. While rock asphalt mastics may, generally, be preferable for the best class of work, the so-called synthetic mixtures can be of excellent quality and service, when scientifically prepared, as is proved by the large areas of successful work in various parts of the country. Certain advantages may even be claimed for some of the synthetic mixtures manufactured by firms of repute, and claims are made for various classes of aggregate in this connexion; but limestone and siliceous limestone have the advantage owing to the many years of experience and success in their use.

It must, however, be realized that all materials within this class are not necessarily satisfactory as aggregates for a limestone mastic asphalt. The softer grades of rock are not, generally speaking, suitable for this class of work; but the ideal is to be found in rocks which are hard enough to give control of the grading, and which, at the same time, produce mastic of good texture and easily handled. Limestones from the lower carboniferous (Avonian) measures are generally considered the best for this purpose; but siliceous limestones, of the Kentish Ragstone type, have given good results in practice.

Both of these classes of aggregate are permitted in British Standard Specification 596 : 1935, and in contradistinction to rock asphalts the limestone must be ground to a greater degree of fineness as is shown by the following limits as laid down in B.S. 1447 : 1948—

	Percentage by weight	
	Min.	Max.
Passing 7 mesh sieve .	—	100
Passing 25 mesh sieve .	75	100
Passing 72 mesh sieve .	40	70
Passing 200 mesh sieve .	30	50

NOTE. The cumulative grading specified above is the standard. For convenience, the approximate equivalent grading by the passing-retained method is as shown on page 165.

LAYING ASPHALT TILES

(Photo: Tecart Studios, London, W.C.1)

	Percentage by weight	
	Min.	Max.
Passing 7 mesh sieve and retained on 25 mesh sieve	0	25
Passing 25 mesh sieve and retained on 72 mesh sieve	5	35
Passing 72 mesh sieve and retained on 200 mesh sieve	10	20
Passing 200 mesh sieve . . .	30	50

It is usually found in practice that the true limestones approach the upper limit of the grading, while the siliceous limestones come nearer the lower limit.

THE ASPHALTIC CEMENT

Reference has already been made to the fact that mastic asphalt consists of two main components, and though the question of the mineral aggregate may be briefly dealt with, it is much more difficult to generalize on the subject of the asphaltic cement.

Whatever class of aggregate may be employed, it is necessary to add bitumen for the manufacture of a mastic; though, when employing asphalt rock, the added bitumen will be less because of that already present in the asphalt rock itself.

When it is desired to employ lake asphaltic cements, the success of the mixture will depend considerably on the choice of suitable flux or asphaltic bitumen. It is essential that the flash point be reasonably high and the percentage of volatile products low. Materials from asphaltic base petroleum are, generally, preferable to those of paraffin base, and the presence of solid paraffins is not desirable as these adversely affect the ductile properties.

It will be appreciated that the number of mixtures which can be prepared with lake asphalt in combination with asphaltic flux or asphaltic bitumen will be considerable. The following table, therefore, refers merely to typical examples, and in practice an almost infinite number of variations is possible.

ASPHALT TILE ROAD PAVING, HUELVA, SPAIN

(Photo: T. Salkield)

TABLE I

	(1)	(2)	(3)	(4)	(5)
Lake asphalt . .	50%	60%	70%	77%	82%
Flux . . .	—	—	—	23%	18%
Asphaltic bitumen .	50%	40%	30%	—	—
Specific gravity at 15° C. . .	1·19	1·21	1·22	1·25	1·30
Penetration at 25° C.	26	21	28	35	40
Softening point .	61° C.	66° C.	65° C.	51° C.	56° C.
Ductility at 25° C. .	40 cm.	15 cm.	12 cm.	45 cm.	30 cm.
,, at 30° C. .	70 cm.	35 cm.	28 cm.	90 cm.	45 cm.
,, at 38° C. .	100 cm.	100 cm.	60 cm.	85 cm.	70 cm.
Soluble bitumen .	76%	72%	67%	64%	62%
Mineral ash . .	18%	21%	26%	28%	29%

MANUFACTURE

In the manufacture of mastic asphalt the incorporation of the bitumen with the asphaltic cement is a factor of great importance.

In the process it is usual to add the aggregate and the asphaltic cement to the mechanically operated mixers, in predetermined quantities. This process is continued at intervals until the charge is complete and the mastic is then left for a specified time at a definite temperature to effect complete incorporation.

The charging and "cooking" periods are dependent both on the type of plant and the material in process of manufacture, and is a matter that can only be settled from experience in mastic making operations. It is usually found, however, that the synthetic mixtures can be prepared in a relatively short period, i.e. from 2–4 hours from the completion of the charge, whereas rock asphalt mixtures may take 4–8 hours.

When the mastic is finished it is drawn off and cast into moulds and the resulting blocks weigh each approximately ½ cwt.

For the manufacture of asphalts of this type, the number of specifications possible with the materials commercially available is considerable, but typical examples of mastic asphalts, employed for paving purposes, are shown in Table II.

TABLE II

	(1)	(2)	(3)	(4)
Lake asphalt	9·5%	10%	5%	18·5%
Flux .	—	3·5%	—	4·5%
Asphaltic bitumen	9·5%	—	5%	—
Asphalt rock	—	86·5%	90%	—
Limestone dust .	81·0%	—	—	76·5%

AT THE SITE OF THE ROAD WORK

The remelting of the blocks or moulds is carried out close to the road work in portable mixers. These mixers are fitted with a stirring apparatus, power driven, and it is necessary to ensure a thorough mixture of the mastic asphalt with the granite chippings which are required to reinforce the mixture to prevent abrasion and rucking under present-day high speed traffic.

The size of the chippings has been the subject of considerable difference of opinion, but they must be free from dust, and range between $\frac{1}{4}$ inch and $\frac{1}{2}$ inch. For general purposes $\frac{3}{8}$ inch chippings may be regarded as the best size.

THICKNESS OF MASTIC CARPET—
PERCENTAGE OF CHIPPINGS

For first-class roads, on a concrete foundation, the carpet should be 2 inches thick. The chippings should not exceed 45 per cent by weight as this has been found to be sufficient for the heaviest types of traffic. For lighter traffic, a coat $1\frac{1}{2}$ inches thick, on a concrete foundation, may be laid. The chippings in this case should not exceed 40 per cent by weight. Where it is proposed to lay mastic on an asphalt concrete base, $1\frac{1}{4}$ inches may be regarded as a sufficient thickness; in fact, for light trafficked streets, 1 inch only is necessary.

IN BRIDGE DESIGN

Mastic asphalt may be usefully employed as a surfacing material for steel bridges, either on plates or trough decking, as it ensures not only a suitable carriage-way but also waterproofs the structure. In this connexion it should be noted that while the coefficient of expansion of asphalt is greater than that of steel, the asphalt is a plastic solid with sufficient ductile properties to absorb the stresses and prevent deformation without rupture.

CHAPTER XXII

NATURAL ROCK ASPHALT TILES

THE tiles are manufactured from a natural limestone asphalt rock naturally impregnated with not less than 8 per cent bitumen, found in France, Switzerland, and Italy, and in accordance with British Standard Specification 1324 : 1946.

The rock is ground to powder, heated slowly for approximately four hours until it reaches a temperature of 140 °C., then discharged from the roaster, allowed to cool to a temperature of approximately 35° C., and is then ready to be pressed into tile form. The pressure to which the powder is subjected is approximately 4 tons per square inch. The sizes are generally 8 inches by 8 inches and 8 inches by 4 inches, the thickness varying according to requirement from $\frac{5}{8}$ inch to 2 inches. They can be produced in many colours by adding the necessary pigment to the powder before it is roasted. The tiles are bedded on fresh cement screed, so as to ensure that they are truly bedded.

Natural asphalt tiles have been laid in various parts of the British Isles since about 1902, and proved to have an exceptionally long life. Natural rock asphalt tiles have also been extensively used in U.S.A., all over Europe, and also in Egypt. These tiles have been used on a large scale for floorings, and are popular as they are made in various colours.

Synthetic asphalt tiles formed of bitumen, crushed stone, and filler are made by placing the materials in moulds and subjecting them to a pressure of 6,000 lb. per square inch, and have been successfully used, though only to a limited extent, in this country. They are made in different sizes, 9 and 12 inches in length, $4\frac{1}{2}$ and 5 inches in width, and from $1\frac{1}{2}$ to 3 inches in depth, according to the requirements of the traffic. These tiles are made in accordance with British Standard Specification 1325 : 1946.

The following points are claimed for asphalt tiles of both types for road surfacings—

1. They can easily be transported from the place of manufacture to the site of work without loss or damage.

2. They can be taken up and relaid with a minimum of loss or damage.

3. They can be expeditiously laid and repaired.

4. Owing to the joints and rough surface due to the presence of the crushed stone, they are not slippery.

5. They furnish a resilient surface, impervious to moisture, and provide a cheap form of asphalt paving of pleasing appearance, which can be laid without expensive plant or the necessity for specialized skilled labour.

6. They are durable, offer small resistance to traffic effort, and can be safely laid on gradients as steep as 1 in 15.

7. Owing to their density, due to the high pressure in process of manufacture, they do not suffer from the extremes of climate and are, in consequence, dustless and sanitary.

8. They are noiseless, owing to their elasticity, and the surface, being sufficiently resilient to absorb vibrations, makes this form of paving very acceptable in the vicinity of churches, schoolhouses, and hospitals.

CHAPTER XXIII

EMULSIONS AND GROUTING

A FEATURE of road making in recent years has been the developing use of emulsions, chiefly bitumen, and their employment for road surface dressing, and for actual construction work. The subject of road emulsions is, however, too complex for an adequate review in this book and the reader is referred to special text-books on the subject, and particularly to Specification No. 434 : 1952 of the British Standards Institution for bitumen road emulsion for penetration (grouting and semi-grouting) and surface dressing.

Emulsions have been defined as "a liquid product in which a substantial amount of bitumen or tar is kept suspended in a finely divided condition in an aqueous medium by means of one or more emulsifying agents." An emulsion consists of two immiscible liquids, one very finely divided in the other. The liquids usually comprise an oil, and water (more accurately an aqueous solution)— in the case of normal bitumen road emulsions the "oil" is bitumen very finely divided in water containing a small quantity of emulsifier.

Bitumen, however finely subdivided, will not remain in suspension for more than a few seconds in pure water. The particles would coalesce and for practical purposes the emulsion would cease to exist as such. The use of the emulsifying agent overcomes this difficulty by reducing the tendency to coalescence and also by making it more difficult for the globules of bitumen to run together.

Colloids are used as emulsifiers—among them soaps, proteins, and colloidal clays. They have the property of forming *adsorbed films* round each globule of bitumen. They reduce the interfacial tension between bitumen and water and in some cases, notably with protein emulsifiers, concentrate round the surface of the globules to an extent sufficient to produce envelopes of considerable strength.

In any case, by the choice of appropriate emulsifiers and by correct proportioning of the material used, coalescence of the emulsions may be indefinitely retarded.

Very small quantities of emulsifier are all that are needed —less than 1 per cent (calculated on the total emulsion) will usually be ample. They do not produce any noticeable effect on the properties of the bitumen emulsified.

Emulsions have a wide field of use for the dressing of all kinds of road surfaces and give a wide range of climatic conditions during which road operations are possible. With road emulsions, however, some attention has to be paid to the climatic conditions and it is useless to try to carry out work in pouring rain or during periods of heavy frost. Emulsions are immediately available for application to damp surfaces without loss of the possibility of adhesion, and when emulsions are applied at the correct viscosity they can be relied upon to hold chippings up to ½ inch or ⅝ inch.

For grouting (penetration) purposes emulsions are extensively employed, as they do not necessitate a great outlay in the way of plant, and can be applied even when climatic conditions are not suitable for other methods.

The stone course may be from 2 inches to 3 inches thick (or more if applied in two layers) and the bottom is sealed off by a thin layer of sand. The prime essential is that the stone course shall be rolled tight before application of the emulsion. This is applied by hand or by pressure tank at 1–1½ gallons per super yard according to the thickness being grouted. The surface voids are filled with ½ inch racking material and the work finally surface dressed after allowing a few days for the road to settle down under traffic.

Road surface formation by grouting methods can be carried out in either single- or double-coat work, as the conditions demand, and by conditions is meant the thickness of the crust required and the character of the traffic.

In recent years the "retread" process has come more into use as an inexpensive means of reshaping worn and rutted roads and providing an even running surface. This method consists of scarifying and regrading the old surface and applying, by means of a spraying machine, a total of usually one gallon of emulsion per square yard in two or three applications. Each application of emulsion is followed by mixing the aggregate and emulsion *in situ* by means of harrows drawn by a tractor. After final consolidation the surface is left to the traffic for a few weeks and given a final surface dressing with emulsion and ⅜ in. chippings. The advantages of emulsions for surface dressing are—

(*a*) Ease of application without heating to give correct dosage of binder without thin spots, and without danger of fatting up.

(*b*) Simplicity of equipment used.

(*c*) Equally readily applied by pouring can, handsprayer, or automotive pressure distributor.

Rates of application vary from 3 to 6 yards per gallon according to the openness of the existing surface and the size of the covering material. When using large size chippings for blinding adequate emulsion must be used to secure proper adhesion.

Rolling may be carried out before or after the set of the emulsion, but if before setting the rolling will in many cases actually help the break of the emulsion. The principal factors which lead to "breakdown" of emulsions are—

1. Evaporation of the water.

2. Chemical coagulation due to the action of the stone.

3. Porosity of the road surface and of the chippings.

4. The incidence of mechanical disturbance on the breaking emulsion.

Double surface dressing is best for heavily trafficked roads. The surface is best cushioned by a first application of emulsion blinded with sand or fine grit, followed by a second surface dressing, when the first has set, using ⅜ inch chippings for final blinding.

PART IV: THE ROAD USER IN RELATION TO ROAD MAKING

CHAPTER XXIV

THE VEHICLE

PASSING on from the study of road making and taking up the topic of road using, we leave the domain of constructive effort to consider destructive operations. As soon as vehicles began to use the few and rudimentary roads which came into existence during the sixteenth century, the element of rivalry between the road maker and the road user began and continued until quite recently.

One frequently hears the remark that there is nothing new under the sun—a statement which must be accepted because we have no means of disproving it. It is, however, open to doubt if ever in human history anything approaching the modern ideas of transport has existed. The ancient Hindoo writings hint vaguely at air transit, and we often encounter in India those who tell us that the heavier than air machine was known long ago in that country, but of roads and road transport nothing is mentioned. But the prophet Daniel was able to visualize our modern conditions very clearly, for as long ago as the sixth century B.C. he wrote that a time of great activity should come, and that it would coincide with an era of extensive knowledge—" Many shall run to and fro, and knowledge shall be increased." In modern parlance this running to and fro is expressed by the one word TRANSPORT—an excellent word, which means to carry across. To-day transport agencies, spider-web like, are spreading over the whole world, linking together by the most wonderful operations all nations and peoples. As the atoms are linked together to form the elements, so is each person a unit or an atom in the construction of that element which we term nationality. Consequently every one is deeply interested in this subject of transport. It matters not how our journey is to be performed, whether by rail, water, or air, it is the ROAD which forms the first and last link in the chain of progression. It takes us to the starting point, and delivers us at our destination. It will be seen that the road, like the vehicle, is always regarded as an active and not a passive creation. It is the road " goes," the road " turns and twists," the road " travels " in every direction. Yet it is the vehicle which facilitates our movements, and enables us to laugh at distance, and to rob the time factor of its terrors.

Throughout the long era of animal transport in this country, when horses, bullocks, and mules were used as pack carriers, there was no big demand for roads, because the absence of such means of communication did not interfere with the economic situation, and the people of those days were able to pursue their ways in a manner which we are sometimes apt to envy.

Therefore, in our own country we do not find anything of real interest with regard to vehicles from the end of the Roman period until the fifteenth century. Contraptions, on one wheel or more, must have been known, and the wheel-barrow, or some form of springless cart for agricultural purposes, must have been made by the village artificers, perhaps on similar lines to the wonderful types of vehicles which are in constant use in the rural districts of India. During the period when Joseph was a great personage in Egypt he was raised to such a rank that Pharaoh " made him ride in the second chariot which he had." Other vehicles for the conveyance of merchandise were also known, for Joseph, we are told, gave to his brethren " wagons " on their departure out of the land of Egypt. In the time of Moses we read that he gave wagons and oxen to the Levites, with each wagon two oxen.

The Romans had their carriages as private means of conveyance, but they were restricted to people of high rank, possibly owing to the narrowness of the streets and the congestion caused by pedestrian traffic. Perhaps, for this very reason, the transport of goods in the streets of Rome was not permitted between sunrise and sunset. The Roman carriages, which appear in representations of public ceremonies, were of slight construction, and sometimes covered. They were generally drawn by a pair of horses, but, when four horses were employed, they were yoked abreast, and not in pairs. Consequently, we can understand why restrictions about the use of the road by the common people had been introduced.

England in feudal times did not favour the use of carriages, as it was supposed to unfit the vassals for military service. Horseback became the general mode of travelling. About the end of the fifteenth century covered carriages were employed on state occasions, but as these conveyances were used, in the first instance, only for ladies of rank, it was regarded as a reproach for men to ride in them. Stow, the historian, who lived between the years 1525-1605, tells us that " Little by little they became usual among the nobilitie and others of sort, and within twenty years, became a great trade of coachmaking." In 1601, owing to the large number of carriages, a Bill was introduced into Parliament, " to restrain the excessive use of coaches," but was rejected on its second reading.

The designer of coaches hit very hard those who produced the ornate ceremonial barges and other craft, which from the earliest ages had been an important means for the transportation of passengers and commodities, wherever waterways were available. The following lugubrious lines were written by John Taylor, the waterman, poet (1580-1654).

Carroches, Coaches, Jades, and Flanders Mares
Doe rob us of our shares, our wares, our fares ;
Against the ground we stand and knock our heeles,
Whilest all our profit runs away on wheeles.

Thus do we see how, in the whirligig of time, changes

arise, and what appears to be the utter extinction of some particular industry is but the curtain raiser to wider human activities.

The introduction of the steam-engine enabled people who had imagination and mechanical skill to produce the most wonderful machines for service on the roads. For a long time progress was slow, and for longer popular opinion was against the new ideas. Railways did not gain immediate favour, and even the Duke of Wellington, writing in 1833, stated—" It appears to be admitted that the railroad cannot pay. . . . . I am rather inclined to think that the work will not go on." Other times, other methods, how true is this old adage! To-day the railroad could not exist without the high road, and the co-ordination between the two is essential for the nation. But the mechanical age had arrived, and nothing could hold it back. The old school of road vehicle designers, who were limited to horses or steam, in the course of time gave place to those who had become acquainted with a much more serviceable agency, to wit, the internal combustion engine, the development of which is one of the greatest marvels of our generation. This invention has wrought a greater revolution than any other achievement which has marked the last 100 years of mechanical progress.

It is very interesting to note how vehicle body styles persisted, and we can trace transition periods. The early railway carriages were in appearance like road coaches, and the earliest road motor cars were similar to the hackney carriages, with an engine occupying the space formerly filled by the hind quarters of the horse. The designer of the modern motor vehicle is the person with whom we have to reckon, as it is he who makes the running and creates the demand for road efficiency. Cause and effect, action and reaction, have each in turn played their part in the evolution of the modern road and the modern vehicle, and it is open to controversy to prove which has produced which. The vehicle designer in the pursuit of his ideal has been moving all the time towards greater resilience and elasticity, and this he has obtained by improved methods of springing, lighter bodies, better load distribution, larger tyres, and certain mechanical devices for the absorption of shock. The shocks to be absorbed may be either sudden and severe, or a series of small ones, set up by vibratory action, which, by reason of their rhythmic periodicity, may be equally destructive.

The very excellence of the vehicle designer's work along the present lines makes him a person of great importance. It would be idle for anyone to attempt to stultify his activities by limiting his field of operations to our roadways as we know them to-day. Had the permanent way railway engineers failed to keep pace with the designers of the locomotive engine, we should not have the magnificent tractors which thunder along our railroads at high speeds, pulling mighty loads with ease. No—the vehicle designer and builder must be allowed to run the gamut of their imagination, skill and experience, so that the evolution of the road vehicle, of many types to suit the many needs, may not be hindered. But we are entitled to wonder if the road vehicle will be improved upon by a tangential departure from present practice. We have moved in a vicious circle in which the road kept overtaking the vehicle, and the vehicle outpacing the road, which has resulted in the uneconomic expenditure of public funds.[1]

The road maker, in his desire to prevent the deformation of his roads by the destructive agencies which are the products of the vehicle designer's skill, developed types of road with more or less rigid foundations. Whether in consequence of this or not—perhaps, partly by reason of it—the designer of the modern mechanically propelled vehicle pursued the opposite course, and aimed at greater

---

[1] This historical reference to vehicles is taken from one of the Author's previous contributions on the subject, and is reproduced by the courtesy of the publisher of *The Road Maker*.

resiliency, and reached a high point of efficiency. Thus, it will be seen, that by that wonderful capacity for compromise which is inherent in our race, although the road maker and the vehicle designer and constructor pursued two lines of action, the exact opposite to each other, they were moving in parallel lines, to produce the results with which we are all so familiar to-day.

CO-OPERATION REQUIRED

We have, however, now arrived at a juncture beyond which this policy will not continue, for it is useless for these two highly skilled professions to operate otherwise than in absolute harmony with each other. The vehicle designer and the road maker have now in their possession the most valuable data, and, although each is for ever striving towards greater perfection, there is no reason why the interests which are common to both should not be pursued in close co-operation. Road transport is becoming capable of operating in wider circles by the development of the articulated vehicle and the newer 6–8 wheeled chassis vehicles; axle loads have been considerably reduced and economy in maintenance effected. For too long a time a course was followed which seemed to recognize no other principle in construction than that of resisting road shocks by means of semi-rigid roads and semi-rigid wheels of all vehicles which travel over them, but individual wheel springing is the latest idea to overcome this disadvantage. The cost of road works alone should encourage the solution of this problem by the better application of scientific principles. That mass is incapable of resisting motion is a truth of which we are fully conscious by the evidences of road destruction, damage to property, and annoyance to those whose residences abut upon the roads which are used by heavy, high speed, self-propelled vehicles, when such roads are not properly constructed. The Motor Vehicles (Construction and Use) Regulations, 1931, helped towards a solution of this disability.

WHO WAS TO BLAME?

Criticism of the road maker often meant that the blame was placed on the wrong shoulders. Too much had been demanded of him. Dissertations were formerly made about corrugations or the waviness of roads, which were said to be caused by the harmonious action (wheel rhythm) of heavy high speed vehicles. Close attention is now being directed to the subjects of adapting the vehicle to the potentiality of the road and the road to the vehicle; and Regulations resulted in the abolition of steel tyres.

PUSHING, NOT HAULING

Notwithstanding the many improvements in vehicle design which have been introduced, we are still pursuing the remarkable principle of pushing and not pulling loads, as the power which is generated by the engine is applied to the rear wheels. Any obstacle, however small, which is encountered by the forward wheels of a vehicle must occur in advance of the wheel centre, consequently backward reaction takes place, causing the wheel to rise from the road, be carried forward by the momentum of the vehicle, and strike the road with a force, the resultant of the factors, weight, speed, and static pressure of the horizontally placed rigid springs. Knowing that this action is taking place every moment, can we be surprised at the rate of road destruction, and the enormous sums of money which are annually required for road construction and maintenance ?

CHAPTER XXV

SPEED AND OVERLOADING—SPRINGS
AND SPRINGING—TYRES—HAULIER
OR CARRIER—SLIPPERINESS

IN respect of speed and overloading, the road user—the vehicle owner—has ever been the enemy of the road maker, but their interests are mutual. It is admitted by all who can take an unbiased view of the position that the maximum weights allowed by the law are quite liberal ; very often they are much in excess of what the roads in many areas can stand up against. It is, however, useless passing legislation if the law is to be disregarded, though certain it is that more facilities are required for checking loads. Far too much time has been spent in laying police traps for the ubiquitous motor-vehicle driver. It would add to the wealth of the nation if more notice could be taken of over-loading and excessive speeds when such vehicles are travelling over roads, the destruction of which imposes a serious burden on the shoulders of the tax- and rate-payers. Recent Traffic Acts have dealt with this subject, and a driver may now be required to draw to a weighbridge, a provision that is being made by many Local Authorities.

The other road users are all deeply interested in this question of speed, for it is the factor which is responsible for many accidents, necessitating an amount of loss and suffering which cannot be determined. The road user should remember that reckless driving—and excessive speed must be stigmatized as such—endangers the lives of others, for, when brought face to face with dangerous conditions, it is not every person who possesses a nerve cool enough to endeavour to escape disaster by some act which can only be induced by presence of mind.

The road maker is co-operating to eliminate the surprise-factor due to blind corners and bends, and the road user must play his part in this important matter. Speed, as already stated, is of course an important item in the problem of road transport, but it must remain subservient to that other factor—the power of control. Granted sufficient visibility, the speed of any vehicle on any road should never exceed the capacity of the mechanical means to bring such vehicle to rest within a distance of not more than 50 yards, and even that distance may, under certain conditions, be found to be too much, which means that the rate of speed for heavy vehicles on many roads ought not, really, to exceed 20 to 25 miles per hour.

In connexion with this question of speed it should be noted that with solid tyres it was ascertained that impact increased very rapidly with higher speeds, and that forces were set up which destroyed all types of road. This increase of resistance due to velocity was tested, and at $12\frac{1}{2}$ miles per hour was found to be three times as great on a worn macadam road as on a smooth surface. With pneumatic tyres there is little increase of impact with higher speeds, owing to their shock-absorbing capacity.

In considering this question of impact due to speed, it must be remembered that the springs of a vehicle are under static compression due to load, consequently, whenever a depression is encountered, the wheels are forced downwards by the combined forces of gravity and the pressure of the springs.

SPRINGING

Notwithstanding the wonderful advance that has been made in recent years in the design of vehicles (moving by rapid stages from the horse drawn conveyance via steam as a motive power to the petrol engine), it is remarkable that so little attention has been paid to the springing of vehicles, although it is a subject that has received a certain amount of consideration. In this connexion inventive brains have been at work. Perhaps the absence of development in this direction is evidence of the improved condition of the highways, and is consequently a feather in the road maker's cap. We continue to be satisfied with the leaf springs, which have done duty throughout the various stages of vehicle evolution. These springs, as used on all types of road vehicles, are fixed in so rigid a manner that circular motion is impossible, and this results in a considerable twisting force in the materials of which the springs are made. Flexibility in spring design for the modern high speed vehicle is very desirable, and the designers of these vehicles must have given this matter a full measure of consideration. We are fully acquainted with the hammer-like action of lightly or improperly loaded vehicles on any but the smoothest and most resilient road surface, and the effect of heavily loaded vehicles is most destructive to both road and vehicle. A departure will, probably, be made in the design of springs for all types of vehicles, but, unfortunately, as soon as we leave the old simple laminated type, a more or less complicated arrangement of springs becomes necessary. A system of springing on more scientific lines may, however, be introduced.

TYRES

The interaction of rubber tyres and springs has received full consideration, for, although each is subject to static force, the recovery after liberation of each is of different speeds. Reduced taxation on pneumatic tyred vehicles drove the former types of steel and solid rubber tyres off the roads with beneficial effects for all concerned. The tyre-maker is certainly keeping pace with both the road maker and the road user.

HAULIER OR CARRIER

Our conservative instincts may, possibly, be retarding developments, as we continue to think too much along the old lines instead of breaking new ground. Let it be admitted that the last word has probably been said on the subject of the internal combustion engine—that wonderful invention in which bulk is so small in comparison with power—and that the chassis of all types of motor vehicles cannot be further improved upon, although they may yield to more flexible design—what then ? Are we to confess that road transport cannot develop except along the lines of the present types of vehicles ? Let us examine this problem. In the development of the railway services we find that, although the tractive agent, the engine, has developed so wonderfully from the original prototype— say " Puffing Billy " or " The Rocket "—the principle underlying the original idea has remained, and this idea is exactly opposite to that of road transport. In the development of the road vehicle we have come to regard the engine, not only as the tractive agent, but also as the carrier. It is a misnomer to style those people who are engaged in the transportation of goods as HAULIERS, for they are nothing of the sort—hauling is a matter of very small account—they are CARRIERS.

In the evolution of the road transport system our calculations have been made on the factor—" Cost per ton mile "—in which speed and load carried play so important a part. Owing, however, to the great saving in time which " door to door " transport provides, the question of speed of commercial vehicles must be given secondary consideration to that of load transported. The resistance to tractive effort cannot be regarded as being proportional to speed, as it increases at a greater rate than the speed developed. Therefore, this plea for bigger loads, distributed over a larger floor area, carried on more wheels, and at a lower speed, contains the real germ of economy, and is being recognized as an important aspect of motor transport by the road maker, the road user, and the vehicle designer.

TRAILERS

With the present type of commercial motor vehicle, it would be impossible to develop the trailer system, as they

are not designed to act as tractors, and hauling would tend
to a more rapid depreciation of the mechanism and wear
and tear of tyres.

Another reason why the trailer has not become a feature
of road transport is in consequence of the speed limitation.
If such a system were encouraged by an alteration in the
speed limit, a tractor might be developed which would
be able to withstand the strains that are set up in starting
and stopping. The development of this system would be
a reversion to the principles which are so well understood
in the horse and cart method of transport. This system
has so many advantages over the mechanically propelled
vehicle, which carries its own load, that it would seem to be
a practical solution of the economics of this problem of
road transport. But the present types of trailers are not
designed to react to the shocks which are encountered in
road transit. Owing to rough road surfaces, and frequent
stoppages, before the trailer system can be evolved it will
be necessary to take up an entirely different view point.
Vehicle designers have considered the subject and the old-
fashioned trailer is doomed to extinction with the development of the "mechanical horse."

As the law at present stands, the regulations with regard
to trailers limit the number to one only, and prohibit their
use for carrying passengers. No heavy motor-car (that is a
car exceeding $2\frac{1}{2}$ tons unloaded weight) may travel with
a trailer at greater speeds than those which are laid down
in the Road Traffic Act of 1934—

	m.p.h.
Heavy motor-car with Trailer—	
Pneumatic tyres all round . . .	20
or Pneumatic on vehicle and soft or elastic on superimposed trailer	20
If trailer not superimposed but on soft or elastic tyres	12
All others	5
Motor Tractor with Single Trailer—	
(no more allowed under R.T. Act. 1930)	
Pneumatic tyres	20
Soft or elastic	12
All others	5

The other regulations with reference to trailers do not bear upon the point that has been raised, but the whole subject is under consideration with a view to the possible reversal of the present system from that of carrier to that of haulier. The law, however, with reference to trailers will not be amended until it can be proved that two or more trailers can travel on the public highways without endangering the public interests. Light locomotives on rubber tyres are allowed to travel up to 12 miles per hour with not more than two trailers.

SLIPPERINESS

Slipperiness, which once upon a time agitated the minds of all parties, was a subject that had been forced upon attention by the different means of transport which had been placed on the roads, and the improved road surfaces which had been developed to meet the needs of the new types of vehicles. It was known from practical experience that road surfaces, under certain climatic conditions, could then become more or less slippery. But many causes, other than slipperiness, are responsible for skidding, such as excessive camber, steep gradients, unbanked curves, corrugations, unsuitable or insufficient brakes, lightness of vehicle. The presence of dirt and oil on a road surface may, in consequence of fog or light rain, cause a greasy mixture to be formed. Great negligence is displayed, and much loss caused, by the dropping of oil from vehicles. On water bound macadam roads, with untreated surfaces, this is quickly absorbed, but on paved roads the circumstances are different, and a drop of oil covers a considerable area. Skidding can be best explained by stating that the force which tends to cause a sliding motion is opposed by that opposite force of friction which exists between tyre and road surface ; and so long as the frictional force is greater than the sliding force, skidding is impossible.

The whole tendency of modern road construction has

been in the direction of producing an impervious surface, which, by reducing the coefficient of friction, makes higher speeds possible, with less tractive effort. In the production of this class of pavement, the road maker and chemist, acting in co-operation, have distinguished themselves, and the co-operation of the vehicle and tyre designers has been secured to overcome any tendency of vehicles to slip on the excellent roads which have been provided to meet the demands of modern traffic. In this connexion the road maker is producing non-skid roads; the tyre maker improved non-skid tyres; and the designer, by lowering the centre of gravity of road vehicles, is helping to reduce the dangers which have been inherent in road transport.

Four-wheel brakes are also helping to solve the trouble, for with this provision it is evident that it is possible to dissipate the energy of motion in half the time that is required by applying the brakes to two wheels only—assuming that the pressure is the same in each case. A very fruitful cause of skidding was due to the too sudden application of the brakes to avoid accidents. Sufficient information has been gained on this subject to make it clear that, with careful driving, complaints about skidding should rarely be heard. If road surfaces of all kinds could be kept clean and free from oil, dirt, and other greasy substances, the causes of slipperiness would be reduced, and all the known types of surfaces would be made safe for all kinds of vehicles.

CHAPTER XXVI

CHANGED CONDITIONS IN RECENT YEARS—ROAD MILEAGE—ROAD COSTS—TRAFFIC STANDARDS

(*Note.*—For the purpose of reference, some chapters of the previous editions of this book, first published in 1927, are retained, as they have historical value.)

In 1900 the total number of motor-cars in the world was 11,000. In 1912 the commercial motor vehicle appeared as a working proposition in this country. In that year the proportion of horse drawn and motor vehicles was as 80 to 20. In 1927 it was 5 and 95 of which 75 per cent was heavy commercial motor traffic. In 1922, in Great Britain, about one million motor vehicles were in use.

The increase in 1924–25, and in 1925–26 was—

Motor cars from—
    345,959 to 425,705 = 23%   425,705 to 498,188 = 17%
Commercial vehicles from
    183,987 to 206,802 = 12·4%   206,802 to 232,482 = 12·4%
Cycles from
    295,506 to 329,292 = 11·4%   329,292 to 338,905 = 2·9%
Motor taxis from
    72,424 to 75,870 = 4·7%   75,870 to 77,424 = 2%

The present rate of increase shows that nearly 2,000 new motor vehicles are being licensed each week.

At present in the United Kingdom we have one car for every 47 persons, but in the United States of America it is one for every 6.

ROAD MILEAGE

England and Wales Class I . 18,262
,,   ,,   ,, II . 11,478
Scotland .   .   ,, I .   4,968
,,   .   .   ,, II .   3.259

The total mileage of the roads of all classes in Great Britain amounts to 177,321. Class I includes all main trunk roads, and Class II all arterial and by-pass roads.

But there is a third class which embraces all the roads not included in the two categories.

In the roads which are styled Classes I and II grants from the Road Fund are made at the rate of 50 and 25 per cent respectively towards the cost of maintenance. The expenditure on the other roads is helped by annual grants from the Road Fund, and the cost of upkeep has to be provided from the local rates. This is a very perplexing matter as these unclassified roads are mostly rural, and were never properly constructed to meet present day traffic demands. Rural roads are 93,938 miles in extent, and of these only 3,394 miles are entitled to grants from the Road Fund under Classes I and II. Of the total number of 651 Rural District Councils, 171 had not received any grant from the Fund since 1st April, 1923, but since that date £5,000,000 has been allocated from the Road Fund for the improvement of important roads in rural areas. As the mileage of unclassified roads is 139,354, it will be realized with what a serious problem the authorities are confronted when it is remembered that 90 per cent of the traffic on the main roads is mechanically propelled, and that this traffic, in consequence of the congestion on the main roads, is making more and more use of these unclassified roads.

ROAD COSTS

Measured by the sums of money which are now demanded for roads, the importance of the subject is at once made manifest. In 1909–10 and 1910–11 the amount actually credited to the Road Improvement Fund was £1,161,345. In 1921 it was £9,432,000, for the year ending 31st March 1924, £14,570,363, and 31st March, 1925, £16,000,000.

The cost of maintenance, which in 1914 was about £17,000,000, is now approximately £50,000,000.

	1913–14	1920–22	1922–23
Cost per head of population for roads	8/8	21/9	21/1
Per £ of assessable value .	1/8	3/6½	3/4

The amount contributed towards this amount by those who pay for the privilege of possessing mechanically propelled vehicles is equivalent to over 1s. 2d. in the £ on the assessable values.

TRAFFIC STANDARDS

These standards have been fixed as follows—

Light Traffic—70 vehicles per day with occasional heavy vehicles.

Medium Traffic—70 to 250 vehicles per day with not more than 5 per cent heavy vehicles.

Heavy Traffic—250 to 600 vehicles per day with 5 to 10 per cent heavy vehicles.

Very Heavy Traffic—Over 600 vehicles per day and over 10 per cent heavy vehicles.

The Ministry of Transport, in a statement issued in January, 1936, stated that—

"The gross receipts from the taxation of road vehicles in Great Britain, including fees for driving licences, etc., during the calendar year, 1934, amounted to £32,588,000 and the net receipts, after allowing for rebates and refunds, to £31,473,000. Licences were issued for approximately 2,395,300 mechanically propelled and 23,000 horse-drawn vehicles. The corresponding figures for 1933 were £29,201,000 gross and £28,357,000 net, derived from 2,282,000 mechanically-propelled and 27,670 horse-drawn vehicles. There was thus an increase of 4·96 per cent in the number of mechanically-propelled vehicles licensed, and a decrease of 17·04 per cent in the number of horse-drawn vehicles on which Excise licence duties are payable.

"It is estimated that in 1934 there was one motor vehicle for every 19 persons in Great Britain and one driving licence for every 14 persons. In 1921, when the present system of taxation was brought into force, the number of motor vehicles licensed was 873,700 and the net receipts in that year amounted to £10,042,000.

"During the financial year 1934–35 the net proceeds of

motor licence duties paid into the Exchequer amounted to £31,538,000, of which £5,100,000 was retained in the Exchequer and the balance paid into the Road Fund. The total receipts of the Road Fund, including fees under the Road Traffic Act, 1930, and the Road and Rail Traffic Act, 1933, and from other sources amounted to £26,975,305.

"Payments amounting to £12,014,170 were made to highway authorities in respect of grant-aided works and for other purposes and a further sum of £6,458,573 was made available to the authorities through the General Exchequer Contribution to local revenues in the form of block grants. At 31st March, 1935, the Road Fund was indebted to the Exchequer in the sum of £2,530,000. Other commitments of the Fund at that date amounted to approximately £17,401,000."

ADDITIONAL NOTE

From 1921–22 to 1926–27 the grants under the Classification Scheme to Class 1 roads were at the rate of 50 per cent, and at the rate of 25 per cent for Class 2 roads. In 1927–28 the grants to Class 2 roads were increased to 33⅓ per cent, but the grant for Class 1 roads remained unaltered. From 1929–30 the grants to Class 1 roads were increased to 60 per cent, and those in respect of Class 2 roads to 50 per cent.

Under the Local Government Acts of 1929, Rural District Councils in England and Wales, and the District Committees in Scotland, ceased to be Highway Authorities.

Revenue from the taxation of motor vehicles, etc., is no longer credited to the Road Fund, and Parliament decides how much is to be paid into the Road Fund every year.

The Minister of Transport, under the provisions of the Trunk Roads Act of 1936, became the Highway Authority for such roads, which, in the First Schedule of the Act, were set out in mileages as—

England	.	.	2,854
Wales	.	.	417
Scotland	.	.	1,188

The Road Fund Report for 1938–39 set out the total mileage of roads in Great Britain as—

Trunk roads	4,456
Class I	23,089
Class II	17,634
Unclassified	135,348
	180,527

Divided as follows—

England	135,614
Wales	18,952
Scotland	25,961

For all information relating to expenditure on the roads and highways of the kingdom, the reader is referred to the Annual Reports on the Administration of the Road Fund.

CHAPTER XXVII

HORSE *v.* MOTOR

BY the year 1914 commercial motor vehicles had been proved to be economically superior to horse drawn vehicles, owing perhaps, in the first instance, to the fact that the element of fatigue in engines is so slight as to be negligible. A horse can only work a limited number of hours per day, but a motor vehicle can continue for a much longer period, in fact, as long as the human element can be provided in regular relays for controlling its operations. In the adoption of the motor vehicle a similar kind of operation can be seen to that which was experienced 100 years ago by those who lived when the change over from coaches, and other horse-drawn road vehicles, to railways was effected. It was really a gradual transition, and many people of those days, and much later, refused to patronize the new method of transport. But the war, willy-nilly, forced our hands, as it became more and more mechanical throughout those terrible years 1914–18. At that time the importance of the mechanical method of road transport was brought home to all concerned in the prosecution of the war. The vehicle existed, but the road was more or less a potential quantity. Many of the roads had been wiped off the map—not a trace of them remained—and those that continued to exist as visible entities, whether partially destroyed or not, had never been designed to carry anything heavier than horse drawn vehicles. Thus, it became necessary to reconstruct all the roads in the war zone, including those within rifle shot, and those roads which formed the lines of communication with the Channel Ports. In the work of road construction the mechanically propelled vehicle, though in itself a cause of destruction, was, by virtue of its increasing output of work, the most important agent in the construction of roads for its own transit. As the railway lines are laid, the constructors push up supplies along the new track from the base for further extensions ; so did the lorry function in the war area.   In this way, and in the absence of horses, which had been absorbed for other war purposes, the hitherto only partially suspected possibilities of mechanical transport became realized ; consequently, it was the war that forced the pace, and made quickly possible what would otherwise, in conservative England, have taken some time to become appreciated, and a longer time to turn to practical use. Being an ingenious people it was seen that, whereas it took years to produce and train a horse, it was possible to fabricate a mechanical horse in a short time, and one that was not so liable to suffer from the rigours of active service. The close of the war saw an enormous number of motor vehicles thrown out of use, and this produced a most disturbing factor in the motor industry. All the recent shows of commercial vehicles have afforded striking proof that whatever pre-eminence was lost at the end of the war (owing to the slump in the building of these vehicles) has long since been regained by us. These vehicles speak volumes for the skill of our workmen, the capacity of the designers, and the business acumen of the manufacturers. Particularly should this be of interest to us, as the home manufacturer of commercial vehicles for a long time received no protection against foreign competition.

MORE AND BETTER ROADS

In the development of our national motor vehicle industries, it is essential that roads—more roads, and better roads—should be provided, to enable the home demand for these vehicles to be sufficient to encourage mass production. In this way only can our manufacturers compete in the markets of the world. We ought to know, well in advance, what the attitude of the Government is likely to be, on the subject of roads, and transport by roads. Unfortunately, as always happens, vested interests may delay progress, and the antagonism between the powerful, well-established organizations which control the railways, and the newer commercial bodies which are developing the road transport systems, cannot easily be brought into line. There is, naturally, a wide divergence of views on this subject, and one can only hope that prejudice, or the influence of the shareholders in the older industries, will not be allowed to thwart or delay the evolution of the newer ones.

Before road development was established in this country, one hundred years ago, many Committees of the House took evidence on the complex problems of those days. After the turnpike system had accomplished its mission and had become obsolete, in consequence of the increased road-borne traffic, all interests antagonistic to progress were swept aside, and the roads disturnpiked.

It is necessary that the local authorities should endeavour to work together along harmonious lines, and co-operate with the other parties to solve the problems which delay progress. And what are these problems? Vested interests, as already mentioned, may be regarded as the greatest of them, and insufficient roads the next important one. Sufficient data on the question of road construction and vehicle design have been collected to solve these problems, and nothing further need be purchased in the expensive school of experience. There is sufficient money, potential and actual, in the road transport undertakings to enable all the parties concerned, if they will only act together, to make a great national success of all the allied industries connected with the subject of road transport.

PASSENGER SERVICES

In 1927 statistics had proved that passenger road transport had grown in popularity at the expense of the railway services. This was to be expected, as, owing to trade depression, it was to this branch of transport that the owners of motor vehicles turned for a remunerative field for the exploitation of capital, which was invested, immediately after the war, in the numerous motor vehicles which had been built for war purposes. It was stated on good authority in 1927, that in this country the number of motor passenger vehicles to those in use for the transport of commercial goods was in the proportion of three to one.

GOODS SERVICES

When we consider the problems connected with the con veyance of goods, we are confronted with a new set of factors. To begin with, although the chassis and components which are used for commercial purposes are very similar to those of the car, the demands upon each are entirely different. The private car is like a carefully nurtured person, conserved, and great care is taken of the mechanism, because it is generally driven by its owner. Its yearly mileage is much less—generally speaking—than its capacity, and it is rarely tried beyond a safety factor of endurance for either load or speed. The exact opposite set of conditions applies to the commercial motor vehicle. It is not always carefully treated ; it is often driven beyond its safe mileage capacity ; drivers are frequently changed from vehicle to vehicle, and, in consequence, as no personal responsibility can be continuous, neglect ensues. It is frequently overtaxed both in load and speed. There is too great a tendency on the part of owners, either through ignorance or otherwise, to show lack of care in the maintenance of their vehicles. These ill-treatments and defects are fatal to the well-being of the vehicles, and detrimental to the roads ; and afford further reasons for closer co-operation. It is as important for the commercial motor vehicle owner to eliminate, as far as possible, everything which tends to excessive wear and tear of his machine, as it is for the road maker to provide a structure that will afford easy running, with the minimum amount of tractive effort, impact, and vibration.

CONFLICTING INTERESTS

In the 1927 edition of this book occur the following passages—

The road maker, in his efforts to provide for the vehicle designer and road user, is frequently in a position of serious disadvantage, owing to the wide range of vehicles and the existing unsettled state of mind in which he finds those who ought to co-operate with him. Two schools of thought are much in evidence to-day—the one requires a vehicle which will be capable of carrying 10-12 tons, and the other is in favour of a lighter and faster type. As economy and efficiency are of equal importance, economy with efficiency is necessary in all types of vehicles. It is quite likely that the final issue will be with the heavy type, because that important factor in all operations—cost per ton mile—will decide the matter. Operating costs are less when the load per driver can be increased.

Co-operation between the vehicle designer, road maker, and user can be secured in other ways, and anything which reduces the time limit, and consequent road congestion, is to the advantage of all parties. The transportation of bulk supplies of commodities can be better performed by specially designed vehicles, which reduce the cost of transport by strict attention to the time factor involved in loading and unloading.

In this year of grace we can see that progress is being made in every direction towards closer co-operation of all road interests.

CHAPTER XXVIII

THE ROAD USER—THE VEHICLE OWNER

WHAT are the demands which John Citizen, the road user, is making upon those who are responsible to him for the highways of this country ?   It is fortunate that no real antagonism exists between these two, although it is not always easy to reconcile the insistent demands of the former with the necessarily slow movements of the latter.   The former demands, but the latter, in acquiescing, has to seek the necessary power to act from the higher and lower authorities.   This entails a time element and makes John Citizen say unkind things about official control and unnecessary delays.   The demands are : That all roads shall be suitable for all types of traffic at all times and under all conditions.   That the surface shall be smooth, but not too smooth as to render it slippery, and that the coefficient of friction shall satisfy the two extreme demands of the man who uses rubber-tyred vehicles and the man who owns a horse and cart.   That the camber shall be as slight as possible consistent with the flow off, towards the channels, of surface water.   That the gradients shall be such that only the minimum tractive effort shall be required to overcome gravitational resistance, of which we are so well aware the moment an effort is made to raise a weight.   This is a most important item, for flat gradients are essential on the score of horse-power consumption and consequent economy which results ; and also on the ground of eliminating the danger element which is inherent in steep gradients. For his personal safety the road user demands that blind and dangerous corners shall not be allowed, and that those now in existence shall, without delay, cease to exist ; that bottle necks, bends, cross roads, and obstructions which impede vision, shall be regarded as anachronisms of an

obsolete past—an immediate past, before the demon of
speed had taken possession of us, as is the case to-day ;
that the amount of dust on the roads (and its concomitant
mud) shall be of negligible quantity.

THE VEHICLE OWNER

The road user, when he is a motor vehicle owner, should be
a sagacious person, to make sure that he is getting full value
for his money, not only from the person who has designed
his vehicle, but from the Authorities to whom he pays his
rates and taxes.   The vehicle owner has to insist that his
vehicle shall be cheap to run, and that the maintenance
expenses shall bear a fair and proper proportion to capital
outlay and output of work.   It is foolish economy to buy a
cheap motor vehicle, if, in the two important items running
and maintenance expenses, the costs should exceed those of
a more expensive vehicle.

The vehicle-owner road user should adopt the statistical
habit, and, by a very simple method, keep a record of
every item of expenditure in connexion with the vehicle.
If this is not done, no means exist for ascertaining whether
the cost of working and upkeep is showing a sufficient margin of profit to satisfy all reasonable demands.   If it is done
with every vehicle, it will soon be possible for the owner
to determine which type is going to give him the best
results, when working over a period of years.   He (the
vehicle owner) should contract with the makers for the
periodical inspection of his vehicles, and to keep them in
a state of repair.   Not only is this a sound co-operative
proposition from the vehicle owner's point of view, but it
also offers a useful field to the vehicle designer, who is able
to improve on his previous efforts, by defects which arise,
and to which his attention is called by expert observers.
In his dealings with the Local and Central Governments,
the road-using vehicle owner can play his part as a free
and independent elector in the careful selection of the
representatives who control the expenditure of the money

he contributes in rates and taxes.   It is to be feared that there is too much *laissez-faire* in this important matter of representation, and that, as a consequence, his interests are not always safeguarded.

The development of the motor vehicle may easily outstrip the road, because of the freedom of the designers and manufacturers from the trammels of official brakes, which is one of the disadvantages the road maker has to contend with in our well-controlled and governed State.   But it is in this direction that the road user must keep on insisting that the road shall be equal to the demands of the vehicles, and that proper co-operation shall exist between the vehicle designers and the road maker.   Both these experts have many problems yet to solve, and the design of the future vehicles may be a departure from the types with which we are so familiar to-day.   It is quite likely that, with a better distribution, it will be possible to carry much heavier loads on more wheels with less damage to roads.   There is, however, no definite consensus of opinion at present on this subject ; if change comes it will be as a result of co-ordinating the ideas of the experts with the needs and views of the non-expert but very practical road user.

INDEX